Susan,
Thanks for be
so happy, Rin
upbeat on a
arrival ♡
Hope you enjoy my
new book
Nicole Xx

In the words of Sir Billy Connolly

I've got a lot to say. And sometimes it comes out in the wrong order. Please don't worry about this. I personally couldn't give a fuck. So don't let it get you down. There's a bit of profanity. But I like that. And I'm rather good at it, too!

WWW.MICHELLEHOGGAUTHOR.COM

ISBN: 978-1-9163248-2-4

I had to quote this because this man has my heart. He's a true Scottish legend and his humour is timeless. As soon as I saw it, I knew it had to be added. Like in this book - if you don't like a bit swearing and profanity, just put the book back on the shelf or unadd it to your basket. I started writing this book when I had just lost my grandad, another true gem, and something just told me to get the fuck on with it.

So, I did. From start to finish this took me 5 years as it was just a little distraction from life that I dived into now and again. Now, as I turn 40, I gave myself the kick up the ass I needed to get this finished, to get serious about what I started and to get this out for others to enjoy as I hit the big birthday. They say life begins at 40 so here I am in all my hot mess.

This is a fictional story, but the main character is based on myself - a single mother raising children and trying to find her way. Fumbling along. Some things have actually happened in my own life and others are totally made up, with a tall tale added. I've always loved writing stories. Even at a young age I'd get lost in my imagination and writing; storytelling is something that just flows to me without any resistance.

I truly hope this finds you when you need a laugh at life. And I hope you find this an easy and amusing read. Even if you aren't a mum. It's not about how to knit a jumper or be a good mum or wife, it's the complete opposite so anyone can enjoy this story.

For all my mammas though - pull on your mum pants, but don't forget you fucking rock! You are beautiful, talented and have a purpose in life. To just be magically, beautifully, fucking YOU.

Thank you,
Peace and love.
Michelle x

Chapters? Who needs those? Just enjoy the read and stick your wee bookmark where you finished off to remind you where to start again!

Problem solved.

Up there for thinking, down there for dancing!

Enjoy x

They say you can have a midlife crisis at some point, so I'm guessing that arrives mid-way through your adulting hood.

I'm now 35. Well, I passed that exact milestone literally 4 months ago. They have gone, and I'm sat wondering if I've been living in a shoe the last 3 of those. The thoughts that keep crossing my mind over and over are...what is the meaning of life? The vast universe in all its glory! But the biggest question of all - what is the meaning of what feels like my meaningless fucking life?

If you've been like me and bought an abundance of self-help books or listened to audiobooks and podcasts galore, you will know what I mean. You try to search for those mind-boggling answers, but all they tell you is to look within, find a good morning routine and be the best you. And you think to yourself, yeah, I could do that, piece of piss. So, you get up earlier for one week, doing the new life do. Then by Friday, after a week of earlier mornings than usual, on top of being a single mum, you realise that they can all just FUCK OFF with their pish advice as you're falling asleep at 5.30pm on the sofa, hours before the kids go to bed.

To truly go after your life's meaning and purpose is easier said than done. They make it seem like a brisk walk in the fucking park. Jurassic Park maybe because it's not Central Park that's for sure.

On top of that, you're now expected to make your kids think the sun shines out your arsehole like a big ray of mum positivity, with magical rainbows and added unicorns, a dash of fairy magic and even a leprechaun that comes tap dancing out of your butthole! All with a big smile on your face holding some warm cookies you baked.

My 35-year-old self is constantly asking herself these questions. They go round and round, over and over, the same things again and again but with no answers. Not even a stupid one appears. Unfortunately, my brain doesn't seem to want to provide me with any relevant answers to my questions. Unless, it's at 11.30pm at night and it's time to shut down, then she decides to fancies a chat about the wonders of life. It's kind of like you're sleeping but with your eyelids are wide open, like a pulled-up window blind, and you've started to randomly think at this precise moment...

Are you in the right job? Did you give yourself enough YOU time today? Did you do anything to help you start living your BEST life? Did you turn off the washing machine at the wall as that can cause a house fire. Fuck. No, you've not. What the fuck is that anyway? Your best life?

The floating thoughts of the laws of the universe and did you attract any extra shitload your way today? Then your brain flickers as a dramatic game show programme begins to play...Stars in their Eyes style.

Starting up with the smoke machine blowing and you're walking through the smoke, clueless to who you are. Man, I loved that show. "Tonight, Mathew I am going to be" and they took on this new avatar. Dave down the road turned into his favourite karaoke king, dressed exactly like them, bellowing the notes out, singing as best as he could. Those where the days. Simple family tv weekends.

My good god women switch off!

I grab my phone and drown out the mind noise with some rain and waterfall meditation. Aaaaaah, relax. Peaceful sounds flowing through my brain, that's better. I'm feeling zen, relaxing now and... what's happening? I start to feel a pain down below that's come on quickly, one that only a middle-aged women can describe. The late-night feeling down below, the one where you're desperate for a massive piss exactly five seconds after shutting off the brain noise. If it's not my mind racing it's my bladder, sending me back and forth to the toilet a million times. And you know that the more you ignore it the stronger it becomes. Those bloody kids have a lot to answer for! A shitting old age pensioner's bladder in my mid-thirties, that's what they've done to me. Most likely you too if you have kids.

Again? Am I really needing to go AGAIN? Having two kids comes at a costly bladder price! Oh no, no, no, why did we never read those leaflets? Remember sitting perfectly in the mum-to-be waiting rooms before getting your gigantic belly measured and being told you're too big, or too fucking small, for your gestational phase? That nurse, so happy to measure the huge mountain stuck on your front. Your eye roll when she starts to predict like mystic fucking Meg when you will deliver. Oh wait, there she goes. Good God above! Rolling off the bed like a walrus with an *exact* due date. I'm hoping she doesn't write magazine columns predicting the future because both my girls were two weeks late!

Even sex education at school was more about sniggering over a condom and a banana than the cost of having a granny bladder in your late 20's. I mean yeah, my midwife mentioned something about fanny exercising but I mean really...have you tried sitting at work, or on a bus, or at the checkout waiting to get served, whilst trying to bash out some fanny holding exercises? Can you imagine holding your fudge muscles like you're trying not to pee and NOT making a face? I think fucking not Selma so off you fuck! People at the checkout desk asking if you are okay in case, you are having a mini stroke!

It's the face that you make when you're putting on your mascara and no matter how hard you try, you pull the most ridiculous face. It's like your eyelashes and mouth have an invisible string that connects them, and they must work together in synchronicity. My point exactly, it's uncontrollable. Just like your bladder.

So, I ask you - what is the meaning of your life?

Surely, I'm not the only batshit crazy mum who sits around contemplating what your purpose on this Earth really is? Apart from the obvious, bringing up your children. Having tits and a vagina and providing for them the best you can, all while scrutinising your own body's appearance daily as its now changed - from high tits to low tits, normal bladder to needing pantyliners if you sneeze. Also, a must on trampolines at any child's party (note to self after said accident).

All these questions spinning around a solar system bigger than
the Sunday Chinese that's just been delivered to soak up your alcohol indulged Saturday night hangover. Unfortunately, the aftermath gives you the beer fear. They must call it that because that's what happens after 30, you can't recall much of the night before, so I guess that's why it's the fear. Fear of the fucking unknown. You just hope that you haven't done any of the following:
1. Voice noted anyone
2. Went live or on your Instagram or Facebook
3. Offended anyone
4. Told anyone what you really think of them
5. Made a complete arse of yourself full stop.
Nope, all good.

Up until 25, I never asked myself such mind-boggling questions. I just went about my young mum duties. I washed my face, fed myself (kids too, that was super important!) then went about my day doing normal stuff. You hit 30 and it's like life just comes along and slaps you with a big "wake up" stick and you're not in the slightest bit ready to go find the answers to these new burning questions.

Here I am, sitting in a carb-filled Chinese coma, with a belly of a 6-month gone pregnant lady, asking myself why I have no self-control.
Jeezo, why am I such a fat bastard at times? Oh wait, can't say that. Negative self-talk is a no-no these days. Self-love. Self-love. That's kind of hard now as I'm needing to physically roll myself off my sofa and hide the evidence in my wheelie bin like it never happened. Let's hope my detox tablets, slim tea, patches, slimming coffee and vitamin tablets can shit me back thin again come Monday morning. Release the fact I've probably consumed a weeks' worth of calories in one fucking go!

Professor Dum Dum and her crazy ass assistant on YouTube are blasting in the background making up life hacks, which obviously my youngest child tries to copy with much mess and many fails. I mean, did those two actually wake up knowing their purpose one day was to become knowhows and hack givers online?

Only thing that's hacked off right now is me with this stupid shit! Why do kids love this so much? The most annoying music plays as they talk in stupid voices. I'm telling you, they should all have hefty insurance cover because the amount of clothes, cut up objects and trip wires placed around my house... I'm due some shitcraft compensation! Especially as my child is now convinced, they are American and are copying the accent constantly. I don't get it, but I guess I don't have to.

A Place in the Sun followed by Friends plays on the tv, while I rub my belly in this self-indulged bubble of promising myself that I'll be good next weekend, the self-chat I've started after being a gutsy bastard. Monday brings a fresh week to start "living my best life" all over again. Damn you Jack Daniels with your smooth Tennessee taste, you've so much to answer for, sir. Followed by the Chinese takeaway, chocolate and fry up this morning. Aw fuck, let's not think about it anymore. Instructions read - take 2 tablets and tea before bed. Let's make that 4 and double up the teabags just to be sure.

It's a new dawn, it's a new day, it's a new life for meeeeeeee yeah and I'm feeling...

Shite. OMG, why does my child still wake at 3/4am? Hurling myself next to her in the bed gets me most likely 2 minutes of deep sleep between 4 and 7am. I wonder why the insomnia starts before sleeping because I sure as shit should be hitting that pillow with a lead head each night at this rate.

How many overactive sleep waves can one child have? Bad dreams, must be her age. Mum nightmares are not being able to say no to a fucking scone when you've hardly slept and you're buying your big ass coffee in the morning with a double shot plus caramel syrup and a dirty stinking weekend hangover!

And nobody comes running to your rescue! You just sit there munching away hoping the sugar will give you a kick like legal mum cocaine.

Maybe we should all just phone a morning mum helpline where three attractive gay men come running to your rescue and make you fabulous, feel good and ready to take on the world!

Fuck, that's a programme! We could all do with that, not just the clueless men with shit dress sense. Yes indeed, we all need these handsome gay men in our life that tell us "Giiiiiirl you look fucking horrendous! Here, get that on and let's do your hair and make-up." Then we'd look fabulous, even if the devil is still lurking inside after our weekend fuck ups and mum wine by the gallon.

Start of a new day, a new week, a new mindset. Kicking off with some morning meditation. Fuck. Fucking fuck face, I've no time now. I've literally slept like a full-on mum zombie for the last 30 minutes of sleep and that's been between my alarm starting and now. Shit. Shitters, shit, shit. Okay, it's okay, you got this! Up, stretch, think positive, this day is going to go great. Not the best start but I am the controller of my mind, my thoughts, my universe, so let's rock this day ahead. Oh, fuck yeah! Drag the little sleep-killer zombies out their beds, stick the kettle on and update my Facebook status. Yeah, I've got this day ahead by the big hairy.

Cuppa in hand, status update on the Facebook wall-of-no-shame to read: "Good morning, all! Starting this week fuelled with passion, morning mediation and a super smoothie!" while a bit of half arsed buttered toast is hanging out my mouth.

Mr Kenco better kick in soon and ignite the fire within me. I need those 5 minutes of coffee happiness to get me through this batshit crazy morning I'm calling life!
Someone, somewhere woke up to a bright sunny morning, stretched, did yoga by the pool, did their positive life affirmations and is walking through the morning like a fucking goddam life goddess right now! And that person is not fucking me.

That's the kind of stuff that keeps me guessing if this is all just a big billy bullshit lie that the online mum influencers show us when really we are all just running around with half a cold coffee, a bit buttered toast and crazy morning hair each day!

_____

But it keeps me daydreaming that maybe someday I'm going to wake up and BE THAT GODDESS. But for now, I'll just be fashionably late for life and turn up looking like I've been
attacked by angry seagulls. Come to think of it, I'm 100% sure those gulls are going to be walking around carrying a briefcase or wearing a high visibility vest and heading to their daily job of street cleaning soon. Those guys are going to take over the world and become your noisy neighbours who you can't give an ASBO to soon enough.

We are on the road, we are moving, we are running through the morning rush hour traffic like snails on a plane. Yup, Mr Jackson may take up a deal on that next film. Imagine the outcome – big, scary-ass snails and Samuel L Jackson covered in slime as they go about hitting all the passengers with their snail backpacks like Dora the fucking snail Explorer's heading up the aisle of the plane. Yeah, can't see that premiering anytime soon. But either way we are going sloooower than the slowest thing on earth! That is one thing I've never got is traffic. It's like everybody in a 50-mile radius is going to the exact same location, at exactly the same time as you, or nothing. Not a sausage nor a person manning a wheel in sight. Go figure.

Eventually, after what feels like an eternity of trying my damn hardest not to flip the fuck out at the kids who are purposely arguing and moaning at each other the whole bloody journey, we arrive.

"Get out, out the car. I love you."

"Love you too."

"Mwah, mwah. Have a great day, don't run you might fall."

"Love you, bye."

Air punch! The morning rush is over, and they made it with exactly 1 millisecond to go.

Life for me has always seemed to be this way. I don't know why but the morning rush around has been like this since I was a child. I was always running late for everything, especially school, and here I am as a fully grown adult doing the same with my kids. Old habits die hard I guess, but we made it so pat on the back and don't think too much about your past dragging its ass into the present. Hopefully the kids grow up and they become punctual, unlike their mother!

Now, I don't know what car you drive, the colour, the seat texture, but my car is a little beast. Oh, this thing is something else. It squeaks all on its own like a cute little mouse. The windscreen wipers have a mind of their own too, they go waving randomly as I drive by and I've no idea who they think they know as we go about our trips, but they do love a little wave every now and again. My hands, of course, are nowhere near the controls. Maybe it's really Herbie and I'm Lindsay Lohan, or maybe my car's just a heap of shite and even the mechanic is confused by my wee Herbie mouse beast. Yesterday the windows decided they wanted to play funny buggers on me - as I pulled the window button up and turned my engine off, they went down. Ok, let's try this again. Pull up the button, halfway down it goes again. What the fuck is happening here? Deep breathing through my nose like a mad rhino! Inhale, exhale and try this again. "Come on car, just work with me!" Pull up, over halfway...yes...yes...aw fuck sakes. Back down it goes.

I'm fully aware I could be attracting this problem my way so let's high vibe and raise this vibration as the morning traffic chaos has obviously lowered it a tad. Think happy, feel happy. This is just a test, all is ok, and this window *will* work now. I'm as calm as a cucumber, I've lowered my stress levels and upped my vibe. My vibe is so HIGH I can touch the sky. Window, you are mine. Let's work together. Now up you go...oh...oh nearly...oh... FUUUUUUUCKK! Ok, fuck off then and stay like that, look like your knickers are half down who am I to judge. Engine off, see if I care.

So yeah, my car. My car's not a fucking dream machine but it gets me from A to B. I've been brought up to not be materialistic and I know that objects do not bring you happiness. I tell you what though, a big, brand-new, sparkling, blacked-out windows, shiny, polished, big bad ass, fucking alloy wheels, gorgeous-looking car, I don't think I'd be unhappy. But you gotta be grateful for what you have if life is to bring you more, right? I count my blessings that I actually have a car to get me to my destination, playing the music I want to listen to, singing along, not knowing half the words, in my zone; instead of squeezing onto a packed bus and sitting next to some stinking guy who obviously never got a Lynx set for Christmas from his great aunt Nora.

Yeah, I'm grateful I've got my own wheels. But it still feels like I'm in my very own fucking life circus and I'm the fucking monkey performing their next trick!

Listen to this, I bet it has happened to you.
The weirdest fucking thing happened the other day, I was struck by the realisation that I am turning into my parents. Yup, it is already happening! There was that moment, you know that moment, when the words you used to hear your mum say to you are now spilling out of your own mouth at your daughters. And it's happening more frequently so the midlife, mid-way marker is already in fast play.
The first massive realisation was when, instead of keeping on Radio One and listening to Calvin Harris, I flicked through the radio channels:

"I'm your private dancer, dancer for money and any old music will do. I'm your private dancer..."

YES TINA! As you're singing away to the only verse you ever remember, that's the moment, that's the defining moment, of knowing for certain that we are all fucked. Your daughter's looking at you like you're some kind of alien lifeform and tells you, "That music is shit. Turn it over." If it hasn't happened yet guys, it will. Just you wait and it will catch you by surprise. Ooooh it catches you by surprise alright.

I've always loved a mixture of music but of course in my day it was 90's music with glow sticks in the air. Or the 80's classics that were playing on the wireless as I came screeching to life out of the dark tunnel and into the light of my mother's vayjay. And, may I add, on time! The only time in my existence so far

that I was on time for any event.

In the 80's the music was great, but all the music from then up to now shows the variety of life. And believe me, I know about the variety of life! When you leave school and start working full time as a salon junior you see it all. I say salon junior, but it's also known as general dogsbody. Running around after hair stylists with their cans of Red Bull or sweeping up mountains of hair. Of course, let's not forget washing people's week-long, not-washed hair (because they knew they were coming into the salon, you see). Scrubbing through the grease? Now that's when you know you've made it one step closer to adulthood. You then wonder to yourself why the fuck you hated school so much.

Washing hair wasn't so bad if you got a shiny fifty pence piece or, even better, a one-pound coin for doing so. You'd go to town on the regular tippers, giving them a head orgasm for it: "Fuck yeah! Massage that head g-spot baby! I feel a fiver is near!" BUT, my bloody good God, the ones whose scalp looked like it needed a scraper over it...or when the water hit their hair releasing the stink of stale cigarette grease...or the ones who left sprinkles of dandruff like the talcum fairy had paid a visit to their hair...that, my friend, is the pinnacle of the hairdressing assistant world.
    The only thing that made it worthwhile was the faces you could pull behind their heads, until your hairdresser caught you and gave you 'the eyes'. Game over for this bokefest of hair washing you would find yourself doing twenty million times a day.

At the age of sixteen I wanted to leave school as quickly as I could get out of there. I hated every minute of that classroom environment; I was like a caged animal. I mean, 'hate' is a strong word but so is the smell of adolescent musk accompanied with your teacher's rank coffee breath so really, the word is allowed.
    That kinda classroom environment could bring you out in

hives and I swear I had them. It just wasn't for me at all and now, looking at my eldest daughter going through the same thing, the real me is like, "Run! Don't look back! Who needs education? It's a load of shit, life lessons and audiobooks babe!" Who even uses half the shit you learn? I have never used a triangle shape ruler to get through anything in life but hey, it must have a use to someone somewhere.

Then mum me kicks in my head and I'm like, "School is very, very important so listen and take it in. You're not there long..." Fuck, I even fell asleep saying that there. But it's true in both ways and unfortunately me and schooling just didn't make an impression on each other, ever!

Until you own your very own teenager nothing and no one can prepare you for what's to come. Even the school of hard knocks just laughs and tells you, "Good luck!" At first you don't see it of that cute little child that you spawned, the one that helped you clean round the house with their little dusters and their baby Henry the hoover. You give in to their cuteness just because they are small and, let's be honest, all small things are cute. You do this remarkably weird voice around small, cute things, as if your tone, pitch and all sanity have just fucked off out a window somewhere. Well, one day that cute little mini version of you (yes you, us, me, the ones who carry said children) is going to follow in our footsteps and sometimes the footsteps are not cute, dainty, designer heels, they are big, massive, fuck-off, hill climbing boots that have been up and over a few dozen mountains. Suddenly your cute little child is growing up and starts acting like you, but it's an answering-back-and-irrational you. One that wants a t-shirt at 100 quid and expects it from doing the dishes once a month, while you're going around wearing the same fucking clothes from 2012 because the only time you really buy yourself new clothes is when you get the 6 monthly, possibly yearly, night out.

Bastarding insta and Facebook are going to see my fine ass looking my best because the old jumper and jeans look is not sexy mum-wear on a night out. Man, I used to wear miniskirts so short I'm surprised I never whistled my own taxi home. You've got to dress up, life's the occasion, right? But on a mum budget Primark is the best for getting a full outfit for £40, including shoes. Yeah, I know, I kind of feel bad that maybe

I'm contributing towards flooding the world with my cheap ass clothes purchases and they're most likely made in a big factory in the masses with no attention to detail. But fuck me, this Mumma aint been out in a while so I fill my basket full of NO fucks and away I go. Yes, life's not fair. And then the cute little child will sulk about me purchasing clothes because I'm not buying that expensive t-shirt for them. I just got a *whole* outfit for less than your tee, missy! Their face of sheer disgust tells me, yet again, I'm a real mum with all this chat. What and who am I turning in to? What have I become?

There are times I sit and ask myself if I was such a dick to my poor mother. My head answers back, "No, you were worse, don't you remember?" That's when I stop her there and say, "Shut the fuck up voice of memory! You don't have to actually remind me!"

The thing about bringing up the mini versions of yourself is that unfortunately they don't seem to come with a handbook. Trust me, I've looked! But even though you have no idea what you're actually doing, it seems to strangely just come to you, like a know-how online hack. One day you just know what to do, even though I don't think humanity ever will know *'How to Raise Kids and Not Fuck Up a Little'*. In general, our kids go around with clean clothes, food in their bellies and smiles on their faces at least half the time so I think we are all doing just fanfuckingdabby. High five to raising kids without a clue! Maybe that's all a part of life's grand plan - for the ones we raise, we raise ourselves too. Now that sounded almost speech-like and uplifting, requiring another highest of fives.

But honestly, if you have children or even stepchildren, that's the very reason they realised that turning grapes into alcohol was the best fucking idea on planet Earth. Wine makers for mommas - you're the man! Or woman! Equality and all that. Gulp.

When Corona ain't just a beer 'n' lime no more!

Corona, the only beer left on empty supermarket shelves all over the globe and do you know why? Course you know why! A fucking pandemic. A global, life-changing, fucking pandemic and poor old Corona beer is sitting there with the fear that no lips will suck its bottle top again after slipping in a wee finger

and popping in a lime. Yup, they named it after a beer the rotten bastards that they are.

Because logically if it has the same name then it's going to have a virus in it?

Of course, of course, makes absolute perfect sense. Then I see the stock of toilet rolls going down. I'll stock up on both bog roll and Corona so I can sit inside my toilet roll fort, drinking my virus named beer, in fear of what may come of this world. Couldn't give a shit about pasta, keep your shells you filthy animals.

But seriously, looking at the empty shelves it's like a fucking apocalypse! If so, fucking shit roll and pasta won't save your greedy souls! I decide to make those three boxes of Corona Extra and ten limes just to be sure. You never know, it may be a cure!

Ok it wasn't the cure; I've just got a sore fucking head and have woken up with toilet roll all over me and a collapsed fort spread across the floor. Hoping that for some reason I've made this all up. I've a vivid imagination, can you tell? I've got to be making this up right? RIGHT! Fuck, I'm not. I've just seen someone walk past my house wearing what looks like a bra on their mouth. Is that a bra? Well, I suppose 10/10 for effort and if it's padded, I mean, winning. It could work! It's kept these puppies in control a hell of a long time so why not keep a virus out?

I feel like this is going to be a living hell and no amount of beer, crystals or bra masks will stop it from happening. Fuck it, hair of the dog. I definitely need it as one of my eyes is completely blurry now. As I pass by the hall mirror to the toilet, I realise that in my beer infused state I've used the throwaway mask I was given at the supermarket to become a drunken pirate! How do I know this? There's a skull and fucking crossbones drawn on it! I've made myself a little pirate patch. As I enter the bathroom, I see half the shower curtain dangling and I can only

assume in my new role of Blackbeard the Pirate Chief I've obviously needed a sail for my ship. I'm now wondering if there's a small ship put together somewhere in the house...

I swear I'll grow up one of these days but today isn't going to be it. Possibly not tomorrow either. And let's be serious, from what I predict, not this year or lifetime.

Life at present seems to be going about with our heads up our arses doing the same old same old thing, saying the same old stuff, until someone you know dies and you realise yet again that we aren't immortal. I'd happily drink a potion like in Death Becomes Her and get my perky ass back and my tits a few inches higher. If I have a drunken tumble, I just pop my head back on again - hey presto! But you see we moan about fucking everything: our house not being tidy, the dishes not being done, going to shitty ass work, driving home in shitty ass traffic to cook and run around, doing it all again the next day and the next day...then suddenly something happens that makes you question EVERYTHING.

Death! A virus! Death of humanity! Or just common fucking sense!

When it happens, you go through such a weird life-meaning transition, all at the same time. It's like, "FUCK ME! We die? We don't live all the time? what the fuck is this? Is this new?"

Why am I going nowhere? Doing the same thing? Because look! Look! Look what can happen. We can just disappear like a bit of dust blowing away in the wind.
Why is it happening? Is this it? Did I make a difference in life?

Did they go somewhere better? Did they do everything they set out to? Are you here for a certain purpose and now that's been filled its 'poof' away you go?

Did they taste lots of different foods? Did they get shit faced and drink different wines in different countries? Did they do that? Have I done that?

You're nodding, right? This is life and I think that if you are of age to be reading this book then at some point you've lost someone, maybe quite a few people. If you haven't, you're a

vampire so tell me your secret!

Mortality brings out the life panic in all of us, along with that sinking feeling about how precious it all is. You realise that your purpose here on Earth has a sand timer to it. My guess is that my purpose could be to write, to reach out to other people and touch them with my words. Or my purpose may be to sit here and drink another glass of wine! Who knows, right? I may even be able to knit jumpers for sheep - it could be any fucking thing! Who knows! Death makes you realise that life must have meaning.

I thought about this all too much when my kids' dad passed away at a young age. What was the meaning of that? What was his purpose on earth, apart from making incredible children? For his life to be cut short so suddenly in an accident it made me bitter about life being cruel and worried that our purpose would never be unmasked int the rat race of life. His death made no sense to me, it never has and it never will.

Oh, why do people you love have to pass? Animals too. That's the sucky part of life and it never gets easier. Each time it gets you questioning things you can't find the answers to. Adding book to Amazon account - 'What Happens After Death?'

No, put that in the bin. For fuck sakes, that will only add more questions. For once I agree with my mad mental thoughts because she's right. Hey, maybe she does know what she's doing?

I'll trust her on this and add that to the bin and instead I'll add 'How to Cook with Wine'. Fantastic, this is going to be a great read.

Homeschooling sucks ass!

"Wakey wakey you little moonbeams! It's time for school of mum!" Yay, air punch! "Who is excited for today?" Well, I'm not either so roll your asses out of bed kids, mum has a coffee made up in the pot I cook soup in for this day a-fucking-head.
Yes, academically I am atroshes and yes, I had to spell check that too. Basic numbers, sequences and timetables look like a foreign language to me so I'm glad I've made it through on my wits and good looks this long.
Back when I was at school if you couldn't understand things you were labelled as either dumb or not listening. As an adult I've questioned all of this as I'm sure I actually had learning difficulties, but they were brushed aside so instead of paying attention I'd draw on my school pad. Now though, teachers seem to assume that because we are grown-ups we know shit or remember said shit from school. Darling, we don't.

Before lockdown I bet certain people would snigger at those in a supermarket packing shelves, calling it a job you don't want when you leave school. Who's laughing now Greta Got-all-your-grades? If it wasn't for Steve packing your shelf in the local supermarket you wouldn't have your lockdown essentials, so I say HA to you Greta. Who's laughing now? Steve's job is now more secure than your straight As. Saying that, maybe Steve in the store has straight As but enjoys his job no matter the title.

Back to the homeschool of hard knocks where adding and subtracting with potatoes is now a thing. Seriously, what is this nonsense? Where's anything about common sense? Maybe show kids how to be a decent human being rather than simply a Greta when they grow up. Where are the lessons about how to deal with the pressures of life? Instead, it's still all just numbers that I don't understand and it's making me feel inadequate as an adult, as a mum, as a human!

WOW, ok, now I know why my kids moan about school. I'm moaning and it's only Day Three. I'm already trying to get

myself expelled or thrown out of my new teaching duties. It's either that or I resort to drinking on the job and get sacked, given my marching orders with no hope of return so I can run away to have a sneaky smoke behind the shed!
"Muuuuum! Where are you?"

Coming, coming. Fuck, caught behind the shed with a cigarette and gin at 11am. Well, it gives them a great essay to write on arrival back to school. 'My Mum - The Worst Teacher and Borderline Alcoholic'. Here, there's a ring to that and it gives them a great topic to learn - alcohol. Never too young to learn how to pour one!

When teacher training is over and you're allowed back out to a restaurant again, in your £40 outfit and a curfew only seen in an American teenage film, you end up catching said virus. How do you catch it? No, it wasn't through the beer because of the name. It seemed to just float along and say, "You. Yeah, you. You're getting it!" Then 'poof' it lands in your face, working its way through your padded mouth bra like the dirty wee virus that it is. And there is fuck all you could do about it.

While we sit here, tucked up in our beds on house isolation, with hankies stuffed up our noses, coughing till the cows come home (and the coughing with a mum bladder? Yeah, you've guessed!) my cats are swanning in and out the house as free as you like. Those two wee gangster cats, swanning around while I leave the door open for ventilation like little cat Kray twins, noising up the neighbourhood. Shades on and a wee cigar hanging out one side of their mouths. "Yeah, keep us in? No chance! We are the Kray cats." In actual fact they are coming in, moaning for food, then fucking off away to Sally's along the road for some salmon and a stroke. Little cat bastards! While we have to suffer alone for 10 days bed bound, housebound and tastebud-less.
I might send them out with little notes on them just for some fun. Make stuff up and see if the neighbours start believing that the cats can write. Or see if I start getting random deliveries because they've done their job properly and passed on the information rather than simply swanning around and losing the notes in next door's shrubbery. Boredom has seriously set in.

I said I'd never be one of those TikTok people, yet here I am – hooked. Snot up to my eyeballs and turning blue from coughing so much because of the tears of laughter running down my face. On my phone a woman with large breasts decides to run down an escalator (that was never going to end well!) trips, rolls, tries to get up, rolls again and ends up with her arse fully out! Oh man, it's setting
me off again. My chest can't take the hilarity anymore. After an hour of wasting my life flicking through TikTok and belly roll laughing, choking my way through others' misfortunes and accidents, I realise the easy addiction I now hold in my hands.

The only time my life could be considered remotely amusing for others to watch is when I get out my toilet roll pirate ship for a drunken adventure. I assume my boring life won't get me far as a TikTok millionaire. Not even my dancing skills would work as I'd surely end up just pissing my pants with my after-children bladder. No, that new puppy is firmly back in the box of crap ideas and the shameless scrolling will have to be given up. Gradually though, as some of it is actually comedy gold. Plus, it's keeping me amused in my time of need. The plan with the cats and the notes hasn't worked. Must be in next door's shrubbery where some little girl will find them when the leaves fall off the trees and think that little fairies have left them for her. How cute would that be! Little fairy letters. I did that for my daughters when they were little so I
know that would be the cutest little find. Oh, wait. Actually no. No. Maybe I should collect them up as I'm sure I've asked for inappropriate things that fairies would not dare ask a small child. Deny it all, that's all I need to do unless my asshole cat has, in fact, taken one to Sally with her salmon. Then I'll be the talk of the town when they put two and two together.

Deny it all. Dennnnyyy. It. Allllll.

The talk of the toon and now it's a boom, lockdown has been lifted. Like many a drunken bum on a

Weekend night out, the quiet streets are abound with noise again, such as the sound of a flock of seagulls.

05.28am Saturday morning and the flying ASBOs are singing a chorus of Wonderwall while cleaning up the remainder of any donner meat left on the streets. Noisy little twats in their high vis vests spreading the weekend joy, along with any leftover salad, everywhere. Well, that's me awake! Now the cat is at the window watching them and is getting pretty excited about catching himself a phat bird. Ok, ok, I'm up for Christ's sakes! I let the cat out the front door while throwing a 'fuck you' finger at the gulls then trod to the toilet. *What's the Story Morning Glory' starts* playing in my head. "Need a little time to wake up, need a little time to wake up wake up, need a little time to wake up, need a little time to rest your mind, you know you should so I guess you might as weeeelllll...what's the story morning glory?" Fuck sakes I'll never get back to sleep now, little cat fuckers and they flying twats.

Only glory so far is the satisfying first pee of the morningafter ignoring its wild calls during the night. Unfortunately, the only thing wild at this point in time is me telling the seagulls to go fuck themselves after waking me from my slumber. Wild fucking times indeed! When will this illness end? I've been bed bound for what feels like an eternity and I still can't taste that satisfying morning coffee or any of the home cooked dinners that my family have all dropped off for us. My brain knows the smell and the taste, but my senses don't seem to agree.
They have a little talk to each other and the outcome is cardboard. Everything tastes of cardboard.

Three glorious weeks later and I can eventually taste my morning witch's coffee brew once again! That joyous warmth that heats up the devil in me now tastes how it's been made to taste, absolutely fucking glorious! Never shall I take my tastebuds for granted again. Back into the full swing of life with a newfound rush of tasting everything in sight simply because I can! Yes, my slack jeans are starting to get a little tighter with all this newfound love for my tastebuds.

What a crazy time. I mean, I felt not very well at all and not tasting anything sucked, but the worst of it was definitely not being able to hug my parents or seeing my mum cry while we stood apart outside. To be sure my mental health has deteriorated, was it worth it all for that?

I feel an anger rise in my body, a surge of the unexplained. Of course nobody knew what was happening
or what was to come of it but those hugs I lost, that connection to others, that lost ticking time can't be rewound. I'm grateful that everyone close to me is ok but I can't quite shake that sad feeling that life isn't in our hands after all.

I almost feel like a robotic version of me lives out each day now that things are back to normal. That shift again back to the question of why the fuck am I here on this planet? What is my purpose? Damn it, where the hell are you purpose? I've been hunting for you for the last few years and you still haven't shown up! Looking under the bed, in a drawer, out the window...Nope, not a thing! Programming set for the day ahead: chauffeur, lunch maker, dish washer and job completer.

Facebook must be listening in on my thoughts again as a suggested post appeared - 'Take up Yoga!' The only thought I'd had was about how to hold in a fart in downward dog position, but I'm open so I'll give this a spin and hope the bum choir doesn't visit! Maybe my purpose might arrive through a quiet mind and a tight bum. Let's try this yoga thing out, you never know it could be my calling. Or the calling of nature. Either way I pack my bag and off I go. 'Power Yoga'. This title sounds fierce, fun and empowering. Power yoga - let's do this!

As I walk into the room the heat smacks my face like it does when you land abroad, when you step off the plane and that weird sensation of heat whacks you right in the chops. That, however, is a welcome heat to smack you with. This wasn't. My cheeks flushed straight away, and my fringe clung to my forehead like a toddler does to your legs. You know it, you drop them off at nursery and they
give you that hug of dread and a look that pleads 'Don't leave me!' but you sure as fuck do. You shake off that mad wee clinger like a piece of fluff and off you scat for 3 hours to do

mum shit. Like yoga.

"Wow it's hot in here!" I say to one of the ladies next to me.

With a weird look on her face she replies, *"Yeah, it's set to 36 degrees in here. First time at hot power yoga?"*

"Oh, first time at any yoga."

The look on her face told me it was time to pray I make it out this class in one piece.

After doing positions that would make you blush in the bedroom and with a face that only could resemble a tangy tom tomato, I made it out alive. Although I most likely looked like a total amateur, drenched in a pool of sweat and accompanied by heavy breathing, I feel alive. There's maybe something in this.

"Hi, can I book another class please? Maybe if you have one better suited to a beginner though."

A few classes later and my impulsiveness kicks in and I find myself on my first ever yoga retreat in Portugal. I don't know if it was the new teacher Andre and his soft tones pulling my new yoga vagina over the continent, but here I am - eating plant based vegan foods which have never grazed my lips before, kidding-on I'm an earth-womb Mumma. I'm eating pulses, beans, fruit and holding in the farts because my body isn't used to so much goodness in one go! I do, however, feel remarkably like the goddess I longed to be, even if it's just for a short time. I'm away from the kids and waking up each day to eat well, stretch my body out and relax my mind. If this gives me the few days of total relaxation I have never had before then it will be worth it.

Over the days I get to know the others in the group. Some of them are total yogis who I could only hope to be reincarnated as - their mindset, food intake, abstinence and cool calm collected outlook on life is fascinating. However, I'm also glad to see that there's a few others that are like me, who run around normal life like a loon. For them, just getting away from the kids and the crazy routine you find yourself thrown into daily is an escape from life. From mum life, from life life. For people like us a normal holiday is usually finding a drink in your hand at 10.30am in an all-inclusive, like a Brit escapee to the sun. This retreat was flipping the norm and I'm all about that right now.

Four magical days in paradise are over and it's back to the magic that is home. You need to escape to appreciate the small things. Having Andre flowing in front of my eyes daily, stretching out his beautiful tanned and toned body, I know for sure I am ready to get back into the world of dating again. Throw out those fucking horrendous, yet comfortable, mum pants and go get my ass into a string and feel sexy. Yes, sexy. Sexy as fuck because I'm coming away with the realisation that my vagina doesn't need to be locked in the dungeon of mum pants just because I'm a mum. This Mumma has dedicated years to those little sprouts, and I need to have fun in life too. Thanks to Andre, my dungeon days are numbered. It's time to get on a journey for myself and this includes dating. Even though the thought of internet dating fills me with fear that's just the way things are going to be, so bring it on!

NO! NO! NO! DO NOT BRING IT ON!

Well, if I haven't seen a male south of the border for a while I sure as shit have an array of images now. What is this!? When I met my daughter's dad it was a normal meeting while we were both out one night. We didn't say "Hi" to each other only for him to decide moments later to get his wanger out and say "So what you think? Fancy a date?" This online thing is absolutely nuts! Pardon the pun. At least it's giving myself and friends a good old giggle, but I don't think I'm ready for this show. Saying that, I've learnt what kinks are so every day is a school day, even for a mum who thought she was wise to the world. Obviously, I've been under a rock for far too long.

The possibility of finding a nice gentleman online may be a harder one than I first anticipated. But I'm not a quitter and with my friends' encouragement I'm pushing through the sea of Willy Wonkas to find a match. Maybe not the perfect match but any match to start with would be just grand.

I swipe right and left to narrow down the gap thinking about how many say "Ew, no thanks," as they swipe past me. It feels so wrong to judge people based only on a first glance. Nevertheless swipe...swipe...swiper stop swiping! Literally feel like Dora the Explorer again on yet another trip with that wee naughty fox who always fucks things up. Match! Oh, ok, let's have a little look closer. Yeah, ok, he's kinda alright. Let me be the first to message so I don't end up with a generic one first. Alpha female coming through! A few messages later and I have managed to secure an actual date. There's been no asking about other apps he wants to add me on, and he hasn't asked to send any weird shit, so I'd say that's a win so far. Let the dating games begin.

It's a few shitty dates later plus one overnight trip before I find out he likes every girl's picture if she has big tits. I give up. What is with social media? Is it stripping everyone's humanity? It's bad enough you have to swipe to connect with them on dating profiles, that in itself is cringeworthy, but across all platforms it's a clown show. I don't understand how men think we won't find out that they are actually just a creepy, sleazy bastard. Like – hello! Girls are literally the biggest private detectives on planet Earth, especially when it's right in front of us to scroll and check who you follow or whose pictures you like. It's not rocket science! We now have a perfect Picasso painted picture of who you are.

So, it's back to the fluffy socks, a Prosecco in hand and a massive bar of chocolate for company. I think I'm gonna eat the whole fucking lot because, frankly, I need it and don't give a shit. I bet sexy yoga Andre doesn't do this crap. Now my brain has said with its little devil voice, "Go creep on his Instagram..." No, no, no, I'm just making all men bad because of the lack of decent ones that have landed on my laptop.

Oh, fuck it. I'm looking.

Aaaaaaaw for fuck sakes Andre! Here's me fluffing your feathers and making you out to be this perfect specimen of a man but after thirty minutes of scrolling through your profile with my private eye spyglasses, knee deep inside your profile, friends and followers, I've found out that you are, in fact, an enormous cock too.

My dreams lie shattered. I can see now why women are bringing Girl Power back and saying, "Fuck this, I'll be happy and single," because fluffy socks, a Prosecco and a blanket across you in your own space, doing your own thing, is far better than the options we seem to be getting as gentlemen these days. They probably wouldn't hold a door open for you, let alone open a car one for you to hop in. Maybe I'm just old fashioned. Obviously nowadays we are all equal but for fuck sakes - what in the James Bond is going on?

Looks like I'll be getting that lovehoney advent calendar for myself as a Christmas gift this year. To me, from me. For my pleasure and costing me a lot less calories. In fact, maybe I could even burn through a few, give a few less fucks with each one gone. Every day a little window gets opened in anticipation, hoping it's a quiet toy so mum can play because it's too cold to just chuck the kids on the street for an hour of 'me time'.

Maybe I should start up a business for women - a toy a day keeps the assholes at bay. Oh, there's a ring to that! Literally a ring...minus a cock. I get away to bed feeling the need to spread this profound new idea to someone who doesn't think I'm crazy. I'll call my mate in the morning. Yes, I will.

After chatting with my friend, we come up with the idea of starting up a lady-only club where women get to subscribe to a 'Toy Story'. Our game plan is to bring pleasure to the lives of single women. Planners open, we start this project with gusto. After three months of hard planning, and the purchasing of some very shady sex toys, we hit the jackpot. I feel like a kid in a sweetie shop, like an adult Charlie in the chocolate factory - only in my story Charlie is selling dildos instead of candy and swinging vibrators around his head whilst chasing away Oompa Loompas.

They were perfect - the price, the quality, the supply. It was like God said, "Here's the perfect partner. Boom!" It arrived like a knight in shining armour. With its soft pink coat and fluffy trimmings for the box, it was Barbie's perfect Ken. We roll out pre-sales and get the hype going but only after jumping through a few hoops. Quite frankly we should have fucking thought of this as 'Doh!' it's the sex market so it's not like we can start pumping them out to influencers like you would an electric toothbrush! We launch and get the most amazing sales in the first month. Unbelievable! But let's be honest, how many of us take less pleasure than we give over the years? No wonder this is selling like fricking freshly baked hot cakes. Girls, we heard you. We knew that this hustle would be worth doing because when you get what you need, you walk different. Literally...

The influx of sales mean that the shitty car has been updated. Yes, my little Mouseketeer has been replaced. Do you know how many times I wished for a better car when the windows wouldn't go up in the rain or when the noise of clattering needed a swift volume up to ignore? This is a dream come true and I can't believe that I've done it all by myself. Me, the mum, the one who always comes last as money was like a revolving door. Yet now here I am, sitting in my brand-new car. What the actual fuck? is this real?

I touch the steering wheel and sniff it. Yes, I sniff it because it smells NEW. It's the smell of leather and hard work paying off and that smells like something worth taking a whiff of. It's bloody wonderful. I've never been materialistic but fuck me, I think I could get used to this. This freshly alloyed motherfucker is going to take me from not being materialistic to why-the-fuck-not. My good God, I feel like I need to stick on some gangster rap, roll down the window and shout out "Heeeellll, yeah! Check this bad bitch out!"

The kids won't believe that this is the car that I get to drive them around in. They are going to be absolutely buzzing - just like my new range of toys. This is sweet. If this is what success tastes like, I'll have it.

The black shimmer I got added to it is gleaming while the pure black alloys with pink trim are looking proper gangster. I never ever thought I would get a new car, but to get a new car that's custom made for me? The gratitude I have right now is off the scale.

I suppose I have those shitty experiences with dating to thank for this moment. I should maybe hang one of my new toys off the wing mirror like an air freshener. Some fluffy dice dick that can swing like a penis pendulum when I drive to remind me of my sexess. Although I'm not overly sure that would be appropriate when the kids are in the car. I could always do a swappable one, like a dick dice that folds back into dice or pulls out to a dick.

Oh my God, I've just had another idea. Ok, where is my phone? I need to phone my friend and business partner as I'm frantically jotting this down. Thing is, she keeps me grounded which is lucky for me as I've a tendency to be like a helium balloon, shooting up in the air full of ideas and nonsense. Some ideas are gold, but a grounded pal is well needed when it comes to love, life and money-making.

With power, comes stress. With stress comes that good old friend we know and love but have a very resentful relationship with - alcohol! Yes, the devil's juice. With the stress of having a new booming business and being run ragged as a full-time mum who is trying to juggle life, one can often find themselves staring into the abyss of the glass half full, then empty, too many nights in a row. Just when you think you have your ducks all in a row, the ducks take a fuck and demand to have a watering hole. Something to drown out the noise that comes from your brain.

A buzzing, white noise. A chitter chatter, ducks quacking. That's maybe why the watering hole is dry, the glass is now empty. You catch my drift? The little ducklings demand the demon, the demon demands to be used, the more you use it the more you find yourself a hot fucking mess. A hot mess who is still has mum life to do the following day.

I enviously watch the tik toks of people being sober and transforming their life; climbing hilltops, chasing through deserts and making waves of positive change. Here's me with my dick empire, an empty bottle and mum guilt. Fuck, maybe I need to get my ass to another retreat. Maybe they can chant the higher vibrational frequency into me to help me find out my true purpose because it doesn't feel like I'm breezing through life. Even with this sudden rush of dick success. The stress of the dick, even without a man attached to it, is killing me.

Why do we not get a roadmap to life when we turn 16? It's like, *"Here's your teens!"* then at 21, *"Here's your next journey, off into your twenties. Enjoy!"* and then another one at 30... you get where I'm going with this. Just a little map to show you would help.

These are your two choices - if you choose this road, it will lead you here; if you choose this other one then it will take you here. Instead of having to constantly pull up your mum pants, doing the do, and wondering what your purpose is. It's a never-ending journey for answers that I wish our ancestors could tell us. I wish we could go into some mad meditation and come out with a lightbulb moment, *"C'mon great aunt Hanny, tell me. I'm waiting. Stop your old ass holding out on me. You're literally stardust and energy now, give us a solid sign!"*

That solid sign was 6.30am with a jump onto my bed. *"Mum! Mum!"*
"Yes sweetheart, what's up?"

"Can we get a McDonald's breakfast when it opens? I was dreaming of getting one so now I want one and I can't get back to sleep because all I can think about is a sausage McMuffin meal."

What the actual fuck? Thanks for that sign Hanny ya fanny! Mum duties first, I get it, I get it. McMuffin incoming, thank the gods they bloody deliver. What is my life? Stumbling towards my morning coffee and tripping up over the cat who's also wanting an early morning McMunchies of his biscuits. At least everyone's happy, funny how food can do that. Food plus caffeine, that other mother addiction I long for each day.

Standing over my coffee machine waiting for the liquid gold I contemplate this life turnaround. Maybe if I change, like really, really change, things might shift? What if I start taking away the vices I have? What if I start to change things up, would the path open up for me? Would I find my purpose? The other half of me? Don't get me wrong being alone is great. Luckily I'm a bit of an introvert so I don't mind the solitude and being a lone parent, but wouldn't it be nice to find someone who sees me? That would be nice.

Actually, that would be more than nice, it would be bloody fantastic. I've not thought about that for a long time. Well, apart from the occasional online conversation that led to a few dodgy dates which made me lock up my chastity belt and throw away the key! But what if I found someone who's not dragging themselves through life like I am, someone who's got the right mindset and strength to make life better and exciting... Jeezo, I've got a big hot looking man in my imagination. I don't know who he is but he's an extremely handsome, with-it guy. Yeah, I'll have you. Shit! My coffee's nearly pouring over the cup amid all my daydreaming.

As I sip my coffee I wonder if looking into another retreat is the answer to finding my feet all over again. It's not taken me long to go from trainers to heels to sliders as I skid down the hill of life. Right, fuck it, I'm looking for a trip away. Maybe just a long weekend to get my head straight, rethink this whole situation and business plan, life plan, game plan, because there's no way I'm hitting forty as a dick-selling, slider-wearing, mum-taxi, crazy cat lady!

Chap, chap, chap! Awesome, that's the Mcfat pants arrived. Yes, I got one too.

Munching on my McMuffin and loading up the laptop I come across a retreat which is not too far a drive. It's over a weekend so granny can have the kids. She's a superstar and loves time with them so this is already ticking a few boxes.

'Eye opening experience, connect to nature and your true self.' Yes. Yes. Tick, tick, tick. 'Find yourself again.' Purchased! Change is inevitable. Sometimes it's a choice and sometimes it's hard but it is inevitable and I'm going to greet it with open arms. Signed, sealed and paid for.

Nervously, I drive along the beautiful country road. The track down to the retreat is almost off road, more like a dirt track, so I'm taking it nice and slow in my plush new car as this baby is still my absolute pride and joy. The trees are plush and green, and I've opened my windows and turned my music off so I can take in the sounds that are flowing around me: the birds tweeting, the air blowing softly, and in the distance I can hear the faint flowing of water. The retreat I decided to go with is a self-awareness one and it promises to tap into any past trauma or experiences; to go back, be aware of the present and then to flow into the future self. I flicked through so many retreats but I kept coming back to this one so I thought to myself that it must be for me. Before I knew it, I had my plastic out and was punching in my numbers. Did I read the small print? No, but what I did read while munching my McMuffin sang true to my needs so here I am, like Alice in fucking Wonderland looking for her purpose down a rabbit hole.

I've never done any kind of healing journey before. Obviously, I've thought about past experiences, but I've always just sort of shrugged them off as bad experiences. I've felt the pain but known that I had to move along with it. Sort of 'pull up your tits and get on with life'. But there's a shift happening. I'm aware of it happening and with my life going round and round like a whirlpool I guess recognising this could be a benefit for me. Better than holding in a chickpea fart in front of a sexy male yoga instructor, that's for sure! I just hope they don't start singing fucking 'Kumbaya' in a circle round the campfire as I don't think that is my kinda jam. However, I said I'd be open, so here I am. Mind you, the ladies running this may need a can opener. I hope I'm not the only newbie on the block.

As I approach the lodge I feel a sense of calm but there's also an undercurrent of nerves. The retreat itself is beautiful. There's a large decking area at the front of the lodge with a long grassy area running down to the open water area. Jesus, is that a campfire? I knew it!

An array of different cars are in the parking area around the side of the lodge - a big badass Range Rover, a cute little mini, a minivan, an Audi Sport car and a total mum mobile. If the cars are anything to go by there's a right mixture of characters here. Now I'm intrigued, who and what am I walking into?

I pull into a space, switch off the engine, take a deep breath and then fondle for my vape for a quick puff. I hope they let you do that here? Well, I'm a fucking adult, I'll decide what I do even if they frown upon it. I already gave up smoking, so this hot stuff is my only vice for a nicotine hit. If I didn't have it my kids would probably have me locked up as my mum horns would be flipping them about like a mad bull in a ring, racing after a reg flag. Actually, they might be into a bit of Ganja or hash here. Well, it was hash back in my younger days so whatever they call it on the street now? Weed! Yeah, they are all bound to be mother earthy types so they can't moan at me for sucking on a vape if they do that type of thing. Here's hoping so or I'll be in the toilet puffing away like a naughty teenager just to get a hit.

After a few good puffs on my vape, I get out of the car and grab my bags from the boot. As I close it behind me I hear a call, "Hey girl, come on in! We can't wait to meet you!" A lady with beautiful long copper hair and a massive smile is waving me over. I like her immediately as she's got a good vibe about her, she reminds me of that girl in 'Brave'. This was a good idea I can feel it already.

The other ladies are chattering next to a table whilst having a cuppa and they smile at me as soon as I enter. All around me the smell of incense sticks is calming. The copper haired lady is called Zoe, and she greets me and gives me a tour of the lodge.

After I have dumped my bag in my room, I join the others for a lovely warming herbal tea. This is nice! This is very, very fucking nice! Wow. I don't know if it's this herbal tea or the incense sticks or what, but I feel super chill. Fuck, maybe it's weed tea or laced with mushrooms or something? Shit. Maybe I should have read the small print! Fuck, why do I never read the small print? I'm like a child just quickly running my eyes over the page, skimming through it roughly and signing the dotted line. Oh my God, is this an actual mushroom retreat? Am I going to be floating around the forest and hugging the trees? All of a sudden a wave of complete panic washes over me and I don't know why. Maybe because now I'm here, my bag is dumped in the room, and I've said hi I can no longer escape the unknown.

Yup, you fucking guessed it! It is a bloody full on 'Herbal Medicine Healing Journey Retreat' not just a bog standard one with deep breathing etc. No, not even close. Oh, there's going to be breath work, but it'll be shroom breath for sure. Only I would fuck up my own 'conquering my life' getaway and end up being the fairy of the forest. Luckily, I'm hesitantly up for it because I damn well paid a fortune for this. Plus, my kids have been shipped off to granny's house for the weekend where, of course, granny always does more than mummy does. That's because granny was brought up with cocaine in her fizzy juice, so she's still got more energy than a Duracell bunny! Mummy sending herself off to the shroom room to sort out her piggin life had better be worth its weight in gold or I'm writing to ask that the drugs be added back to our fizzy juice. Then we can multitask like mofos and not be in the slightest bit bothered by life.

Day One wasn't actually so bad. There are no drugs going around yet so that's a plus, instead we all got to know each other a little and opened up as to why we were there. I may have had to make up a little story along the way because I didn't read the small print and realise the herbal part wasn't just chamomile tea bags.

However, everyone is lovely, and the tea has helped me open up a little. I'm not sure if it was laced, it could just be that hearing other people be so open has allowed me to be as well. Of course, I've had to add in a little extra 'openness' to cover the fact I didn't REALLY know what I was signing up for.

The walk we did was lovely and ended in us sitting quietly in nature, fully at peace, and just listening to the sounds. Feeling the grass on my ass and hugging a tree is actually quite a relaxing experience. They help us breathe and I love a hug so I'm sure they do too!

That evening we had a beautiful meal prepped for us and chatting with everyone openly was amazing, they were such a lovely group of people from all different backgrounds and walks of life. It was truly special finding out about everyone. This adult time with no alcohol, no kids, just peace and relaxation with this group wasn't so bad after all.

The controlled drugs are due to start tomorrow so tonight I make do with puffing on my vape - no having to hide it after all. Someone had a weed one which I turned down because I didn't know if it would affect my experience the next day with whatever it is they throw together. It's supposed to help you deep dive into the trapped parts of you and allow you to release it, but that's tomorrow's adventure. My blueberry flavoured nicotine vape would do the trick tonight.

Over the few days I did some crazy shit that I never thought I'd ever sign up for. Like. EVER! I chanted, I cried (full on snotters too) and I tried mushroom-controlled therapy which was the most profound experience I have ever had in my life. It was like I was at one with the grass and the trees could talk, I know they weren't actually having a fullblown conversation with me, but at the time I could understand them, their feelings and their purpose on this earth. I held others closely, closer than I've ever held someone before, and they were strangers only 48 hours ago. We laughed as we jumped into the open water stark naked and the feeling of absolute freedom in that moment was something I wanted to hold onto forever.

There were also things that came up in my mind that I never thought had any effect over my choices and everyday living, but here they were coming up to bite me in the ass so that I was aware of their existence. I knew I had to take action and talk about them in order to start to heal and understand the role they played in my life to date.

I didn't want to leave, I wanted to stay in this bubble a little longer, but the work that we had done over a few short days was truly fucking life changing. That said, I was worried about what my circle would think of me doing this. What would my family think about the fact that I know in my heart I've walked in one person and in just one weekend I'm walking out with my eyes wide open, wider than they've ever been, to a whole new world. Will they think I'm crazy and weird now? These intrusive thoughts floated around my head, but the tools we were given over the weekend showed me how to control them. I know now that it's the subconscious mind playing out old worries and I simply had to let them wash over me like a wave or allow them to float on by like a cloud. Acknowledge them but don't attach to them, something I've never been able to do before. I'd normally have a thought, attach some other thought to it that was a little more aggressive than the first, then before I know it a whole fucking scenario is playing out in my head like a frigging story in a tv soap. The Eastenders theme tune playing as my thoughts spiral out of control. It was going to be an ongoing task of catching those little thought fuckers as they start and letting them pass not attach.

I might be able to do this, but my family will think I'm absolutely batshit crazy!

As I hug and wave my goodbyes to everyone before my drive home, I feel more at peace than I think I've ever felt before. Certainly more peaceful than I can remember. Your brain can't think about the entirety of your childhood and everything you have encountered, just snippets of it, and unfortunately sometimes it's the shit bits it seems to remember.

Sometimes the only thing that jolts your memory back to the positives are the pictures you reminisce over which help prompt a flickering memory of the good times. Thank goodness we had actual photographs back in the day, I don't know how many pictures or videos I've lost in phones that have been damaged. There go those memories! Thank fuck for Facebook which pops up with memories that remind you of the good, the bad and the downright ugly! Have you ever looked at an old Facebook post when it pops up on your memories and think to yourself - who the actual fuck is the idiot that wrote that? Oh, it was old me. Twat! If I could I'd shake the younger me now, look her square in the eyes and, like one of the ghosts from 'A Christmas Carol', say, "Come with me," I'd zoom her away to show her the future her. Then I'd plant her back in the past with a bit more knowledge on how not be a Facebook post fool. Or a fool full stop.

On my long drive home, I thought about everything that had happened over the weekend and how I wanted to implement it. One thing I know for sure is that I want to rediscover who I am, what I want to do with my life and what I want to let go of. I don't know how my business partner is going to take this but I'm not sure dicks are my future, not the ones in fluff and plastic packaging anyway. I just feel that I have more to give, more to show the world of myself. The business was purely for financial gain and as a struggling single mother it's been a blessing that it's skyrocketed, but after what I've just been through, I can't see this venture being part of my future. My kids are going to benefit from the money, but they won't benefit from how it's coming in. If they or their friends found out where it was coming from they would be mortified! I know I would if my mum was selling dicks for a living. But then if she was rolling in plastic cock cash maybe I would turn a blind eye or give my friends a discount code to keep them from being offended.

So, what is my new purpose? It took me long enough to get into the entrepreneurship of the cock party so this could take a while. I'll throw it out there and ask for signs. I'll ask for the way to be shown. If the trees could talk to me when I was in this state of consciousness, then it's worthwhile keeping this new-found portal open and letting the universe guide me. It's not going to be an overnight shutdown for the dick plantation so I have time. Time to figure out this new version of me. It's like being a newborn baby - first you're born and then you start to get to grips with your body. This kinda feels like that. Or it's like looking at one of those magic-eye pictures, only seeing colours at first before focusing until you are able to see the vision clearly. A way will open up, I know it will. I trust in the universe to help me with my direction. The business takes up so much time with only a small team on hand, so something has to give. Either the answer will come from a sudden rush of knowledge and guidance or through the opportunity to sell the business to pursue something else. Either way, I am of the firm belief that I trust in the flow of magic and fate.

Seeing my kids again after a weekend away I felt so much deep love for them. They are my absolute world and it made me realise what a blessing it is to be a mum, to be called 'Mummy'. To have one purpose that you are so sure of which is to be there for them, every little step of the way, throughout their whole lives. What an incredible thing it is. Challenging, yes, but always incredibly rewarding. My own mum had an amazing dinner ready for us. I'd sent her over a recipe for an awesome Hungarian mushroom soup and she couldn't believe that I had been munching on them in a different way over the weekend! Lucky for me my mum's a bit of a closet hippy. When you start her reminiscing she always slips up with a few memories of magic mushies at festivals from the 60's or 70's. I know that she's no saint, nor sinner either, but she knew how to go with the magical flow in her time and is open to hearing about new things. Even if she doesn't quite get it or understand it, she's a diplomatic person and knows to let each person live their own way.

After telling her all about it and sparing her no details, she comes out with, *"I hope you don't start doing that instead of alcohol every weekend. I'm not coming to save you if you see a pink elephant!"*

I laughed and said, *"You know, I'm actually thinking of trying to go alcohol free for a bit, see how it serves me."*

This shocked her more than the drug weekend I'd just attended. Her reaction made me even more determined to give it a real shot. Not my normal shot, an actual shot. A go. A chance to see how I feel without the vice that's held me up through every uncomfortable situation. Actually, even every comfortable situation. The good old rum has held me up in everything I've done. Well, my pirate days are over! For now, anyway. Time to anchor down and see how I go with this new life flow. Even if it's just to keep this new portal open to see if I can manage stress without a drink. It's too easy to grab a glass after a long day when the kids are settled in bed, and it's something I've done their whole lives. Doing it all alone it's sometimes the only thing that's there for you at the end of a long day. Wild but true.

Sobriety has always been something I turned my nose up at. Why would someone not want to drink? Drinking is fun! Unless you're an alcoholic, then drinking is like breathing with a demon on your back. But I've always been the life and soul of the party when I've had a drink. Miss chatty pants. A bit of Dutch courage before going out to get the party mood flowing. I could never imagine myself as a non-drinker, it just never crossed my mind. To be perfectly honest, I thought they must be sad not drinking. Maybe that's an absolutely ridiculous thought to have but you can't help your thoughts, can you? Well, ok, you can, but that old programming you've got up and running from how you were brought up is deeply ingrained in you. If it's never been a problem before and if everyone does it, then why wouldn't you? Now, looking at it from a different perspective, I think why would you feel you have to?

Every single argument I've had in the past – drink has been involved. Every silly thing I've ever done - drink has been involved. Every single argument I've had in the past – drink has been involved. Every silly thing I've ever done - drink has been involved. I remember seeing a quote: *"If you change the way you look at things, the things you look at change."* Fucking genius. So simple yet so profoundly true.

Looking at this from the same view but a different angle, it makes sense to give it a go.

The two months I have been free and clear of the devil's juices have been pretty fucking amazing so far. Admittedly at the start it was like Nightmare on Elm Street with Freddy visiting me every night; the sweats I had, the dreams I had... Oooooh the dreams. My good Lord I wish I'd written a dream journal. The past was coming back to haunt me in my dreams. The cravings, the grumpiness, breaking the habit of just doing it. Giving up alcohol was manageable, but it gave me a hard glimpse into what it was doing to me and my body. If I was only a binge drinker I'd hate to think what more hardened drinkers would feel with the drink leaving their system. However, after a few weeks I felt totally in control over my new routine and now I felt addicted to the good I was feeling. There was a sense of accomplishment and freedom, of satisfaction and direction in my life again. I got a kick from the discipline of feeling good and of living fully in the moment with nothing holding me back. Nothing was getting in my way for self-fulfilment from now on and it felt liberating.

Unfortunately, with every high comes a test. My test was in the form of my child self harming, something I had never dealt with before. Suddenly a wave of helplessness was crashing all around me, drowning my every thought and action. When the ones that you bring into this world feel hurt or lost or confused and that the only way to cope with these feelings is to harm themselves...well, it's the worst thing you can feel as a mum.

When it comes down to your kiddos you know you will wipe the floor with anyone or anything that gets in their way, mum bull horns and all.

But with mental health issues it is like trying to skate over thin ice, worried that one crack will bring everything crashing down. I've never felt so alone. Is it only my child going through these difficult times? Why can't I stick a plaster over it and make it better? That's what mums do, right? They make things better. The alcoholic in me was screaming at me to grab a drink and fuck off the past few months of personal growth and shroom expansion experiences, to go get my pirate patch back out of the drawer and get one on ice, just to dull the ache of not being able to control this new situation.

Fuck it. I grabbed a glass, poured an extra-large measure and gulped it down. As soon as that liquid warmth hit, I felt my mind mellowing and my body escaping from the thoughts that I was useless. I poured another. The second didn't feel as liberating as the first. Instead, it brought guilt, along with its overnight bag, and I felt like crying into my glass. You've undone all this good! The slippery slope was there for the taking but I wasn't prepared to sit on the sledge and 'wheee' my way down the hill. I put down my glass and pulled up my mum pants. There's got to be some sort of help out there for my child. This situation is not going magic itself away and I am not prepared to dull myself with alcohol. Not this time. Not this fucking time.

I picked up my phone and started researching any help that was out there. To my surprise there wasn't actually that much and most services that were available were overrun, with waiting lists that were months or even years long. Unless you went private you were in for a long wait, so I guessed that private was the option on the plate. I felt sad for others who may not be able to afford private healthcare, especially when it came to their mental health. If mental health problems are on the rise, why is it so difficult to access help?

My brain wanted to research everything, and it felt like a deep dive into a rabbit hole. By the time I had looked at what felt like every single option, I had signed up to a course on mental health awareness and coping strategies. Light bulb moment - is this my calling? Helping others out?

There's so much that's changed in this world after the great reset of Covid. Everyone's lost, I know I've felt it. That feeling of being lost is still within me and self-harm comes in many forms. Even social media is harmful if you get sucked into it negatively. We are so addicted to our devices that we are hateful to ourselves, our minds and those around us. We don't communicate like we used to. On the flip side, when things go Pete Tong at school for the kids they can't just come home and forget about it, they get pulled into group chats and hounded online. Years ago, we could come home and forget that shit filled day never happened and brush it off. But that old saying 'just brush it off' doesn't hold substance anymore. What a fucking stupid-ass saying, 'just brush it off'. No, don't brush it off. Speak about it! Open up to the feelings you feel, get it off your chest and face it. Don't run away and don't brush it off. Heal it. The hurt, no matter how minor, is an issue that, if left, manifests into something much bigger in your head. Your mind's a dangerous place to live with unhealthy and unhealed thoughts, like a loaded gun that's ready to fire at any point. It comes out in all sorts of ways, from masking or hiding it all the way through to eventually harming yourself physically. The more I think of this, the more I start feeling passionate about the subject because the world needs light. A beacon beckoning us towards change before it's too late.

I write down on a piece of paper in my notepad - *'What is my why? My passion driven purpose?'*

I get sorted for bed as I feel totally drained after everything. As I lay in bed, I run over the questions again in my head before sleeping - what is my why? What is my passion driven purpose? After everything I've done recently, what direction is the arrow pointing in? What is the path of least resistance? What is the road I should be following?

The road shown was not clear at all. I had a feeling I was Dorothy in 'The Wizard of Oz', skipping down a yellow brick road to see a magic wizard who turns out to be a scrawny wee man hiding behind a big head that breaths fire and his ego. Which I think was the case in the film - wee man syndrome with added big balls ego.

On my quest I'll get attacked by flying monkeys and my snazzy red shoes will get stolen by a hater with a big nose and bad dress sense. Girrrl, all black and baggy clothes ain't doing you no favours. And that hat? Not doing you any favours either. Just saying! All I want is to go home to safety again, but I'll end up having to click my sliders together three times because my beautiful sparkly shoes have been nicked.

The path of least resistance looks like climbing Kilimanjaro from where I'm sitting. Thanks universe, you never make things easy, it's like looking at signs back to front and upside down without my reading glasses on.

Healing yourself is one thing, healing others is something else. But I'll be dammed if I don't follow my instincts on this one. So many times I've dulled down that inside talk, that pull inside to change direction, to run out of an event, to leave a relationship, to go look at something, to do what your soul's whisper is telling you. I've always fucked it off, ignored it and I suppose that's why I ended up in a healing circle of mushrooms! This time I'm going to go with this whisper I'm hearing, this pull in my belly to stick on my ruby slippers and skid into this full throttle. I never do anything by halves so full speed ahead as the house twirls around and touches down in the magical land of Oz.

After looking at different healing methods available to learn, the ones that stood out to me were the ones that some would say were more 'airy fairy'. That's where the pull leads me as the concept of working with your own natural energy fields seemed fascinating. Something that's not seen but is felt? Now that's cool as fuck. I've never known that this type of healing was out there and available. I suppose unless you know about it already you don't.

This time I looked over the costs of the courses and the benefits they offer with a finetooth comb before deciding I would do go for it and dive into this new world of healing. It may help me to connect with others who are trying to understand how to navigate life's difficulties, for themselves or their own children. Maybe I'll find a connection that they use or maybe they'll know what can help.

I've never thought of myself as a healer. I don't even know what a healer should be like, I just never imagined it could or would be me. I've been on the most raggedy life journey myself, so how could I possibly help others? As these impostor syndrome thoughts go around in my head a quote pops up on my timeline.
It reads:

'The universe isn't looking for actors, it's looking for the real, raw and honest to lead the way.'

Well, fuck me, there's my answer. The universe is guiding me through my socials it seems. So, I push aside the imposter thoughts and click to purchase the two courses that are appealing to me. My stomach flips a little at the thought of going into something so alien but if I'm going to help my children understand their own wounds, I need to keep addressing my own. I need to understand how to heal mine so I can heal theirs.

Being uncomfortable is a good thing, that's what they kept saying at the retreat. On the other side of fear is love. On the other side of discomfort is growth. I'm here for it all.

Stepping into the room on day one of the course I could smell a strong smell of grass. Not like a freshly mowed lawn, the stuff Bob Marley would have while writing his music and speaking to three little birds outside his doorstep. As I think of this analogy the rest of the song plays in my mind - "Don't worry, about a thing, 'cause every little thing is gonna be alright." I took a deep breath and relaxed with that mellowing tune playing in my mind. The smell wasn't actually grass but it sure as shit did smell like it, it was burning sage and man was it strong. However, it cleared my mind and relaxed me deeply which I guess was the reason for filling the whole room with its pungent smell.

It was hands-on from the start, which I loved. Theory was never my strong point as my head finds it hard to concentrate so this was perfect for my learning style. Already I felt like I was at the exact place I was supposed to be, learning in a way that's best for me to absorb all this knowledge. Looking back to my learning in school and what I could take in or how I would interact, I realise I had absolute signs of ADD or Autism or something under that umbrella. Back then it was all swept under the carpet. If you weren't having complete and utter meltdowns or going fully off the rails it just went undiagnosed. Now, as a fully grown women with tits, a vagina and a mad mind, I wonder how the fuck I have managed up to this point. I spotted it immediately in my own children because there is so much more awareness around it, so I suppose as long as I can help them then it also helps me in the return. I just feel sadness that the help wasn't available to me when I needed it and I wonder how many adults have spent a lifetime wondering why they don't fit into some circles when they are really a square.

Learning that we have energy veins that run through our whole-body systems was mind blowing. It makes so much sense. This is like the magic of the unseen, and I love that! We sometimes block these energy veins which causes negative effects in our body, so learning to unblock them can literally lift your whole nervous system back to its natural rhythm and give you an instant feeling of peace. This is magic, why haven't I ever heard of this before? It's like flicking a light switch on again. It's so easy and it works instantly. I believe the Japanese art of knowing this - Japanese monks are the knowledge of the earth, shown through the way they live. They know the magic; I have no doubt about that.

After a light lunch it was time to let the healer and teacher work with you one to one in order to have this magical power working on you. I was a little nervous awaiting my turn and as I watched others coming back in the room I noticed that they looked lighter, upset but lighter. What the hell was going to happen in there?

Snotters and tears was my answer! Snotters and tears followed by an electrical charge running through my body. The sensation was like someone had held their hand down hard on the top of my head and then when they lifted it off it felt like my brain was floating. What just happened there? What was that? A cleansing of the soul? Afterwards the teacher sat in front of me, pulled her beanbag in close and held my hand, *"Are you spiritual? Do you believe in the unseen?"* I replied honestly that I hadn't been up to this point but that something had pulled me here and whilst I'd like to believe, my logical mind wants evidence. It wants the "When I see it, then I'll know" which I know won't happen because I'm being asked to believe in the unseen.

She smiled sweetly and said, *"You have had a lot of heartache and tests in life which have brought you here. You know that, don't you?"* My eyes widened, how is this possible? I think that this woman has dived into my soul which is weird on so many levels. *"You have a very strong connection to the other side. You have spirits protecting you all around you. Look for signs and keep open, you have something very special about you. I know that you can make a change in this world."*

There I go again, crying like a three-year-old who's just dropped their lollipop on a hairy carpet and now it's all covered in fluff.

After an amazing but exhausting day, I got home to the kids and my mum, the saint, has another home cooked meal ready for me. How I love my mum's cooking. There's nothing better than having someone else cook for you, it's a love language that I adore consuming. With fresh eyes I felt like I was floating outside of my body, looking down at my precious family, knowing that the time we spent together doing the simplest things was full of love. I don't know what I would do without this amazing woman in my life, she's been my backbone when things have gone wrong and the light when things are right. I'm so lucky to have this, right here, right now.

Once the girls were settled down, we shared a non-alcoholic drink (or five) together and whilst listening to a few old classics on Alexa we spoke about taking a trip abroad, just us girls.

Embarking on an adventure of self-discovery would be a chance to make some memories and I might get some clarity over where I want to go business-wise. Scrolling through a few packages we found a cracking deal for seven nights all-inclusive in the Canaries, with a free child place included, at only £500 each. We couldn't have clicked on it fast enough! £50 deposit, pay the rest in a few weeks and fly out in two months. Perfection! I'll have finished my courses, I'll have time to sort a few finances and it will take us all away from the usual routine. Above all, taking a girls' holiday that will allow us to relax and reconnect as a family might give my daughter a little breathing space, allowing her to ease her mind about the problems that she's experiencing. I can't remember the last time we did this. Well, apart from a recent camping trip where it rained for two days straight with the sun only arriving on the day we were leaving. The great outdoors in the UK, eh? This trip abroad will be just what the doctor ordered – plenty of vitamin D and good food on tap.

We popped some Erasure on and had a little sing song in the kitchen to celebrate. Isn't it funny how just thinking and acting like you're drinking alcohol and putting on a few feel-good classics can trick you into thinking you've actually had a drink. I don't think my mum is converted to the alcohol-free lifestyle just yet, but she's embraced this bottle or two like a champ and it seems to be working its placebo effect magic tonight. At least this time we will remember booking a holiday in the morning.

After a few more intensive and interesting weeks, I have a raft of certificates stating that I have passed all my therapy courses with flying colours. I feel secure in my newly discovered understanding about how we click and work as humans. It's scary to think that I've fumbled through life so far lacking in this knowledge that I've now had the courage to learn. From the beginning of that mushroom retreat to doing these courses it's something I've never seen for myself, but here I am, a woman of the world, full of love and knowledge to share.

I'm also super fucking excited to have this holiday with all my girls coming up, a sun filled getaway to relax and have fun in the sun. This is exactly what the doctor ordered, I can't wait to step off that plane and feel my worries just slip away. That holiday heat smacking me in the face as if to say, *"Hello, you have arrived at your destination. Please switch the fuck off."*
Of course, holiday time is arriving quicker than I gave myself time to prepare for, so I find myself throwing the suitcases on the bed and hurriedly getting packed for a sunfilled week.

I can't wait to feel that bright orange warmth on my face and my feet sinking into the hot sand. My non-drinking days have disappeared and I am enjoying alcohol again but this time I have a totally different attitude towards it. Having time away from it and allowing myself to get through boredom, stress and social events without it has allowed me to break away from the crutch of depending on it too much to make me feel more confident.

I feel almost at peace with it, that I can enjoy it in moderation and not have a negative attitude towards it anymore. With a sigh, I pack in a few bikinis. Normally the bikini wearing would give me the fear of getting my half-naked mum body out on show, but recently I've started speaking loving words to myself about my appearance and body. It's a love language just for me and in doing so I realise

I don't give a shit about what anyone else thinks. I am me, perfectly imperfect, and I love and embrace all of me. My hot mum ass is ready to turn from blue to pink from the incoming hot weather, leaving this rotten rain behind for a week of making memories with my beautiful mum and kids. I can't bloody wait.

The only downside to my fun-filled adventure is the stress of no longer having a business partnership. My friend wasn't coping well with the stress of the business anymore and didn't want it to impact our friendship so suggested we wind things up on her end. I agreed, knowing that it had been my idea and I had just dragged her along for the ride. She's been a blessing in disguise since day one but with me being unsure of how it would work anymore, if I even wanted to follow this journey or leave the company to go down a new path, she had to think about number one. I completely understood as I know the stresses and strains that come from juggling life and a business, without adding friendship into the equation. Plus, she's been picking up the slack while I've been doing work on my inner soul-searching. We sorted out the finer details of the full handover to me before I jetted off. We made sure the stock was up to date so orders were fulfilled through our online retailer and so everything would go smoothly while I was away on holiday. Everything else can be dealt with once I'm back again. One day at a time is my new motto and the holiday breeze of warm air is telling me to switch off from the madness of life for a bit.

The flight was a long ass one but luckily it passed by quick enough, nothing that a few episodes on Netflix, packets of nuts and games of cards didn't solve. The bus that took us to the hotel had the most talented driver – he could whistle any song perfectly. It's the weirdest talent that I've ever come across but fuck, did we laugh the whole way to the hotel. I don't think I've ever heard anyone do anything like it before or since, it was like a greatest hits album but instead of singing he loudly whistled every single song, he even had a Spice Girls one. We ended up playing 'Name that Tune' on the journey as we tried to guess what one he was doing.

I thought to myself that he should have one of those albums you see randomly popping up on adverts at Christmas time - 'Whistles from the Bus - A Compilation of your Favourite Classics'. I giggled with the thought of this little driver handing out his CDs to everyone who got off the bus. When we arrived, everyone gave him a round of applause for his efforts and entertainment. It was hilarious.

The hotel looked like Bedrock from 'The Flintstones' from the way it was almost carved into the surrounding stones. It was beautiful but also quite strange looking compared to the standard white hotels you would normally get. The entrance was grand and full of glass and large ornaments, which I thought could stub a toe or two in your flip flops after a few too many at the all-inclusive bar and their 'Cocktail of the Day'. We got our wristbands on, dumped our things in our room and headed down to the pool area for a check around the facilities. We wanted to see if the bar staff were friendly and maybe grab one of our first drinks before lazing in the sun on a lounger.

Aaah, this is the life. The sun filled Canary Islands, a warm breeze passing over my body every now and again whilst the girls play together in the pool without a care in the world. I absorbed the sounds of their fun filled laughter as well as the feeling of being lighter that comes from being far, far away from your everyday reality. I headed over to the little supermarket to surprise the girls with the biggest unicorn float I could find. Weirdly, there weren't any in the pool so I thought to myself, 'Just wait until this arrives, they will freak out! Miss Pride Unicorn coming through, all multicoloured with cup holders. This is a bad ass, bitch-energy unicorn right here.' Although thank fuck the man in the supermarket had an electric pump to get it fully up and ready to grace the pool with her wonders, because the air in my lungs wouldn't have blown up the horn.

Flippity flopping my way over to the pool area, wearing Lauriana the magical float (yes, I named her already) around my waist, I realise that it's not actually that easy to walk in flip flops while inside the ring of a giant float. Of course, while I'm not looking as elegant and graceful as I normally would be, I stumble across the path of what can only be described as a god! Yes, a fucking god! He had tanned skin, dark hair and a smile so bright I was glad my sunglasses were tinted. Plus, his tight shorts made it clear that he was Tarzan to my Jane. Fuck me, I thought, what a stunning specimen of a man. Trust me to stumble into the path of a rugged, sexy man when I'm literally wearing Lauriana the fucking unicorn, arms spread wide trying to carry this hoop on my hips. Now, I don't know if it was Lauriana's fault, the flip flops or his smile, but I caught the toe part of my flip flop on the path and flipped arse over tit. I was glad of the soft landing that came from headbutting the back of the unicorn's head as I fell to the ground. Oh my fucking good God! Please say he was distracted and did not just witness my fall from grace!

"Are you ok? Let me help you up."

FUUUCK, he did. Of course he fucking did. How could you miss that display? I'm here an hour, and already I'm causing mayhem in paradise in front of beautiful people. Yup, first prize tit award incoming.

"Thank you so much, I can't believe I just did that," I replied, laughing to try and brush off my absolute shame.

"Well, maybe the unicorn needs some riding lessons. First time out with her?"

"Yeah, it is. I'm just glad the guy in the shop blew it up so much that I literally bounced back up off the deck."

We both laughed as I dusted off my legs from the fall and engaged in a little lighthearted banter. *"Thanks for the hand up. I'm now taking my fall shame for a swim and a cocktail."*

_____

As he walked off with a smile he said, *"I'll hopefully catch you and your unicorn for some fun later."*

What was that? Did I just have a twinge in my minge? It's been a while. Ok, maybe a year or two, or three, but who's counting? Her down town obviously is when the right man lands in her space. Oh my gosh, the heat between us! And that energetic feeling rushing between my legs! I hope he does like unicorns because me and little miss mischief here are up for some fun on the pull. I mean, in the pool. I think I handled that quite well despite the fact that I fell over like I did. If I saw that happen to someone, I don't know if I would be able to give the poor fucker a hand up for laughing my ass off. The fact that he didn't do what I would have done and helped me in my time of need made me like him already. Opposites attract and all that jazz.

A few cocktails later and me and my girls are jumping on the massive inflatable unicorn like crazy monkeys, giggling and throwing each other off it. I love this feeling of joy, of being so carefree and like a kid again with my kids. It's so nice just to have fun without trying too hard to create it, just being in the moment and riding that wave of utter madness and fun. It's so good for the soul. Mum's up by the side of the pool doing some kind of salsa style dancing with the oldies. Look at her go! She's still got it, my mum. Actually, she's never lost it, although I do think the cocktail of the day has probably helped. That and the fact that she's always up for a good time. I've always admired how she goes for things without holding back or being embarrassed, I think I'd have to down the cocktail of the day, the cocktail of the next day and the cocktail of the day after that in order to have the courage to get up with strangers and shake my hips where all eyes could be on you.

I looked at her, looked across at the girls playing and having fun then I sat back on the lounger again, smiling. It was a smile that feels like it lights you up from the inside at just how lucky you are. Even if finding my life's meaning and purpose in my mum pants is still very much like having a Spanish satnav in the UK, leaving you with no idea of where you are going, this moment of living in the now and just being was beautiful.

Mum took the girls up to the room for me so they could start getting ready for dinner, leaving me in peace to sip the rest of my cocktail with Lauriana beside me. I lay on my lounger with my eyes closed, feeling the last of the day's warmth on my face. Hold on, why's it suddenly went dark? Is that the sun away already? As I open my eyes to check, I see that Tarzan is standing in front of me blocking out the sun.

"Hey! How were your day's adventures with the mischievous unicorn? Did you get her under wraps with no more injuries?"

"Yeah, she behaved the rest of the day. I think we've bonded after that fall," I giggled. We have a little chat and he asked who I was here with and where I was from. We then had a little drink together at the bar before both heading back to our rooms to get ready for dinner. It was the most natural conversation I think I've had in a long time, maybe because I spectacularly broke the ice with my fall. Maybe it was a meeting of fate.

The food in the hotel was amazing, not at all like the stuff I've had before in previous hotels where the food was bog standard and tasteless. The chefs here were top notch and even the kids loved it. What was even better was that you could go up and pour yourself a glass or two of wine on tap, it was heavenly. I'd never normally eat as much as I did but I found I was munching my way through everything.

I think that due to the way we are wired as humans when we're presented with a buffet and its array of food, we just keep grazing like cows in a field, munch, munch, munching away. Luckily, I'd packed several floaty style dresses as the food baby that was going to pop out as a result of all my munching, greedy bugger that I am, needed to be kept under wraps. Everything looked and tasted so good, plus the fact that you don't have to prepare it, stand over it and cook it yourself gives you a feeling of appreciation, which makes you need to try more of everything. Stuffing the last piece of cake in my mouth I spotted Tarzan from earlier. I saw that he dressed very well for a guy, maybe too well for a chilled holiday with friends. Wow, his friend is also absolutely beautiful! Not an eyebrow hair out of place, so presentable and clean with big boss vibes radiating around them. He gives us a friendly wave and his friend looks over and gives a lovely genuine smile.

"What lovely looking men," mum says as she sips her wine.

"I know, right? They are so immaculate. That one is genuinely nice too," I replied, as I proceeded to tell her how we met earlier and had a lovely conversation.

"Only you would fall arse over tit inside a unicorn in front of him," she laughed.

"I know mum, I know. Always giving a lasting impression everywhere I go."

The girl that crash landed a unicorn in the Canaries. Spreading a little glitter everywhere I go.

Later that evening they joined us at the bar. The girls were up at the evening entertainment together as my mum and I sat chatting. Each guy was polite and shook mum's hand as they asked to join us. They said they were having a relaxed evening and that it would be a pleasure to be in our company for a few drinks before they headed up to bed. Apparently they had a big meeting in the morning. I didn't have to say too much as mum started to tell them all about me. She wanted to share how proud she was of me. Sitting back and listening, I thought about how it was so touching to hear her say those things to other people. I suppose when you're a single parent you don't think too much about what you do, you just get on with it and deal with things as they come along. However, these guys had an aura about them that made you just want to speak openly to them. They heard all about my struggles, the highs and the lows, along with the fact that I'd thrown myself headfirst into a cock company and was now trying to find my spiritual path to self-development.

They seemed to be impressed by everything they were told. I was waiting for the cringe to come when they heard about a few things, especially the pink dicks, but they laughed and said, *"You found a problem to solve, that's where the glory in the game is."* That made sense to me as I knew I wasn't really doing something new or radical, I had just found something that was missing in the old. I wasn't trying to recreate the wheel, I was just tweaking it.

They invited me along to their meeting the next morning which they explained was more of a talk where everyone would share nuggets of wisdom and take notes away with them. They were staying in the hotel as it also had meeting rooms so they could have a relaxing holiday as well as work. Even as they spoke, they didn't give too much away which made them even more intriguing. As Tarzan stood up, after telling me his actual name was Josh, we all got up and gave each other friendly hugs goodnight, wishing each other a good night's sleep. Before he left he reminded me, *"Tomorrow at 11am. Take the lift to the very top floor and go along to the plaza meeting suite."*

As they left, mum turned to me and said, *"Do you think they are partner partners as well as business partners?"*

I had been thinking the same, but who knows. My man radar is so far off at the moment it's lost in the Bermuda Triangle!

As we retreated up the stairs to head to bed, mum said, "Oh, I forgot to ask about the kids' club. I'll catch up with you and bring extra water back up too."

"Perfect. I'll see you in the room," I replied.

The girls were shattered after their first full day of playing and excitement, so I gave the youngest a lift on my back while the eldest held onto her sister's leg. *"Did you guys enjoy your fist day?"*

"Yeah mum, it was great! Thank you for the unicorn, she's the best fun ever!

As I smiled, I thought about how easily pleased children can be. What a great first day all round - happy children, good food and meeting some lovely guys too. Even if it had been the weirdest of meetings. *"The unicorn is the best, isn't she."*

After breakfast, I had a quick play in the pool with the girls and a coffee with a splash of brandy and cream with mum. So lush. Mum and I sat in the sun, drinking our coffees and chatting about the meeting I was going to attend.

"I wonder what it's all about? You sure I should go?!"

"Bloody right you are missus! I want all the gossip when you come back. Although maybe get yourself dolled up a little. You know, do your hair and pop a wee bit of makeup on. You don't know what you're walking into, so put your best foot forward. Ask the desk for a notepad and pen too."

"Yeah, that's a good idea mum. Up there for thinking, down there for dancing," I laughed. I love that saying.

I sipped the last drop of my new favourite coffee before giving the girls a wet kiss from the side of the pool. *"Right, that's me off. You sure you are ok to watch them again?"* I asked mum as I gave her a quick hug and kiss.

"Are you seriously asking me that? Go get your arse up those stairs and get ready! I'll see you again soon. Enjoy," she replied.

Back in the room I got myself showered and dressed. My pen and notepad were sitting next to my make-up on the chest of drawers and as I got ready to slap on a bit of mascara and lip gloss to finish off my day look the thoughts going around in my head were getting more and more intense. What if I'm walking into some full-on fucking orgy? Like, seriously, I could be walking in there and they could be set to sell me off to some high-scale drug lord who's ready to whisk me off on his speedboat because he's got a thing for clumsy unicorn ladies. Or what if they make me walk along some catwalk in order to get picked by leering men with buzzers in their hands, ready to go to the highest bidder. I do, however, think that's from the film 'Taken'. Plus, my mum's no Liam Neeson so I'm pretty fucked if that scenario was to actually come true. Fuck, fuck, fuuuuuck! What am I actually doing? Why the hell did I listen to my mum? She's probably hoping that I'll find my knight in shining armour instead of the tinfoil covered ones I seem to land back home.

After having a final look in the mirror and fluffing my hair, I grab my bag, notepad and pen and head off to the dungeon, I mean the top floor plaza, for whatever is coming my way. Please be sexy knights or playboys, I'll take both, and notes at that!

I arrive at exactly 11.01 and Josh comes over to greet me. The room has chairs all laid out towards a stage, whilst in the back corner there's tea, coffee, nibbles, fancy water with what looks like cucumber in it, and wine. Yes, I've spied the wine. It's a lovely big spread for everyone's enjoyment.

"So, tell me then Josh, what is today's enlightenment? I've been wondering about it all morning and waiting with anticipation; are you doing a special session or a talk?"

As he started to reply, guests started to appear. *"Shit, I need to go over to them. Just take a seat here, I'll be back in two minutes."*

Jeezo. I'm now sitting there, smiling away, without the faintest idea about what's happening. That wine looks like it needs to get opened, Spanish-style, by noon because I can feel the nerves coming in. I know I'm just a guest along for the ride but I'm wondering why. Maybe he just needs my honest opinion as I'm not a part of whatever it is they have pulled together. They probably just need an outsider to be brutally honest about what it is that they're doing. Yeah, that's what it is. Must be. Only logical explanation, I'd say.

The room started filling with lots of different faces, some very businesslike, some quite relaxed and some at a stage in-between. I felt like a bit of a spare prick at a wedding but since my adventures over the past year have been pretty wild this is a walk in the park. Just as my thoughts floated off again Josh arrived back over. *"I'm so sorry for leaving you, come and grab a water or wine, or both, and take a seat next to Steve at the front."* I didn't ask any questions at that point as I was fully into my going with the flow state and the situation felt, weirdly, abnormally normal.

Obviously on my way to the seat at the front I grabbed a cucumber water and a wine. I'm still on my holidays and a guest at this function so I'll most certainly take both drinks on offer thank you very much! I take my seat next to Steve who is just as beautiful as Josh. I'm sure I said but man, they are both just so handsome! I could look at them all day long. Maybe they could do with a pervert receptionist at whatever firm they work at who just answers phones and looks at them all day, I'd be up for that job! Sipping my wine, I cross my legs and look towards the stage area. I'm feeling excited and I don't even fucking know what for yet!

Well, fucking well. If it's not two men launching their new online dating platform to the world. Just my luck. After falling arse over tit in front of them I must look that down in my dating luck that they've taken pity on me and summoned me along to this prestigious launch for a platform that's about to go worldwide.

To be fair, what they've managed to achieve so far is absolutely incredible. I thought my rising cock company was doing well, but this is mind blowing. As they talk through what they've done so far and how quickly they have scaled it up to go worldwide, my jaw is on the floor in awe of them. Looks and brains? They've got to be batting for the same team, if you know what I mean. They probably want to buy up my product and take it to the gay community. I'm now convinced I've not a sausage hope that Josh is my Tarzan and I'm his Jane.

As they talk about the crazy connections they've made, I wonder how they even managed to connect with such big-name investors. My business partner and I started our company with just us and an online space. We had to hunt about for connections to make our product, then our box and then all the branding. You must have a wild drive behind you to make what they have happen. As they take questions from the crowd of people in the room I turn around and noticed a lot of press cameras at the back taking pictures.

Suddenly, I hear Josh saying my name. *"Steve and I bumped into this amazing woman yesterday and after that chance meeting we wanted to introduce her here today."* He then proceeded to tell everyone in the room the exact story of how we met. I blushed and laughed, as did everyone else in the room. The next thing I knew, Josh was ushering me up onto the stage to stand next to him. A wave of panic swept over me. I'm not good at speaking in front of a room of people, it takes me back to those school days of getting your name called out and all eyes swiveling round on you. Suddenly everyone in the room was turning to watch me get out of my seat and make my way up onto the stage next to him. I shyly put a hand up to say hi and gave my best 'I'm in control' smile to the room, hoping that my flushed face could be passed off as too much sunbathing on pale skin.

Josh grabbed my shoulder and announced, *"We will be partnering up and helping to bring her company to the forefront worldwide, along with our dating site. We were so impressed after hearing her story, its highs and its lows, and we know the guts it takes to launch something that's already available on the market but to give it a unique new twist. It is incredible to hear about a single mum looking for a better life, and we have such a strong admiration for her that we think our support will help make her dreams come true. When you see that rare true quality in someone, and it doesn't happen often, we both knew that she had fallen off her magical unicorn for a reason."*

By this point my jaw was fully on the floor and my eyes were as wide and round as the Earth. They must have looked like I'd just dropped a disco biscuit from back in the day! I couldn't believe what was happening, I felt like I had to pinch myself in the nipple just to make sure I was here and hadn't mistaken a brandy coffee this morning for a mushroom tea again! What the actual fuck is happening? The press started calling my name and asking to hear my story. I laughed, *"How far back to do want me to go? How much time do I have?"* Everyone laughed as they called out, *"It all!"*

Josh whispered, *"You've got this babe, we are both here. Tell them, this is your time."* With that Steve gave me a thumbs up and I took the microphone.

I'd also had to confront my own mental health struggles and my sense of feeling unworthy as a parent - who am I to bring up my children alone?

I'm a shit show half of the time and the other half of the time I don't know my own arse from my elbow so hey ho, how will that go? I'd had to wrestle with the feelings of constant failure at being a mum whilst trying to be open again to including anyone else in the secure little life I had made for us. I didn't want just anyone coming into the unit I had built, that's sacred. No man will fill their dad's shoes, but it would be nice to have someone come in to fill my needs. Who would that be? I don't even know anymore.

I told them about my recent experience with my child's self-harming and how I'd struggled whilst looking for help to navigate this new landscape. Seeing your child hurt so much that they hurt themselves is one of the worst experiences in life, how do you navigate that? Is it even a thing that you can navigate?

Then I moved on to talking about having my breakthrough idea after failing dismally in the dating world. I was honest about not knowing how to get out there and be open again whilst admitting that as a woman we all have needs that only a real-life man could meet. I explained that I'd settled for the next best thing, and that I didn't seem to be the only one who had with how big my business had grown. There was a lady at the front who I could see was shedding a few tears as I spoke and I knew that she'd been through similar, that something I've said has connected with her.

I finished off by laughing about my mad mushroom retreat and ending up here on a whim with my mum who I explained was my absolute hero. I just couldn't have been where I am today without her. At that, Josh got up and walked to the side of the room, put his arm around someone and brought my mum up to the stage. At that point I absolutely broke down in tears. They were happy tears, but I was totally overwhelmed by the whole experience of sharing my story for the first time with what felt like the world. As I looked out at the audience, I saw a room full of people standing on their feet and clapping. I put my hand to my heart and said thank you to everyone, then took my seat at the front beside my mum and Steve.

"What just happened?" I asked my mum?

"Fate," she replied. *"Fate, my beautiful girl. I'm so proud of you."*

"Where are the girls?" I asked in shock.

"With the kids' club. I organised it all so don't worry. Just relax and take it all in."

At the end of the presentation Steve and Josh whizzed mum and me round the room, meeting connections, shaking hands and drinking some much-needed wine.

As the room emptied, Josh came up to me and gave the biggest hug, lifting my feet off the floor. *"You were absolutely incredible, but I knew you would be. I'm so proud of you. Sorry we didn't tell you, but your mum said that you wouldn't show up if you knew you would be put on the spot. Your fight or flight would kick in and flight would win making you miss this opportunity. So, we went behind your back to make sure you'd show up."*

"How though?" I questioned. *"How did you both know so much about me that you wanted to help?"*

"Well, after speaking to you I bumped into your mum and asked if she would give me a few minutes of her time as I wanted to find out more about you and your business. Call it a hunch but I knew there was something special about you when we first met, something endearing, and man was I right!"

Tears filled my eyes again at the unreality of the moment. It was almost unimaginable for something this good to happen to someone like me. We arranged to meet up the next morning so that I could have the night with my girls and my mum to take it all in and celebrate.

"Tomorrow we plan, then you can enjoy the rest of your holidays," Josh told me. *"Once you're home we can start this whole ball rolling because once we start you won't stop."* When I saw the girls, I burst into tears once more. *"Mum? Are you ok? Why are you crying?"*
"Aw, I'm fine. I just love youse so much. Now, who's first in the pool? Mum, grab the cocktails, I'm going in!"

Meeting with Josh and Steve the next day I felt as though I was still in a bubble. We sat down and planned out a few of our next steps to just lightly get the ball rolling and to get some handovers in place for setting up a factory. *"Will you be ok to travel when we need you to, it might be last minute? The family can come as well, of course. We know how much it means to you to show them that dreams can be a reality so don't worry, they can come along for the ride whenever you need them to."*

"That is when I shall speak to my beautiful mother," I replied. *"I am sure we can come to some sort of plan. Just leave that with me."*

Steve then pardoned himself as he needed to go and sort a few things out. *"I look forward to building an empire together as soon as we are back to reality,"* he said and, with a polite hug and a kiss on the cheek, off he went to another quick meeting, leaving me in the safe and beautiful hands of Josh. Man, I know I have to be professional but I'm daydreaming again of him swinging through the jungle in his Tarzan pants and sweeping me up to his tree house to bang me like a jungle drum...

Back in the land of the now I blush slightly at my rude and intrusive thoughts. He must pick up on this sexual energy I am feeling, it can't be all in my head. It's like a searing heat but an illicit and forbidden one. *"Would you like to go grab a quick lunch and a few drinks together now? Let's wrap up this meeting stuff, we can deal with it when you get home. let's have some fun and relax."*

"Perfect," I say. *"I'm game, let's go explore."*

After an amazing lunch and a stroll along the beach with a cocktail in hand the conversation is flowing naturally. It's like I've known him so much longer than I have. Feeling relaxed, I can't help but blurt out, *"So are you gay? Because you are just too good to be true. You have everything all figured out and you are just so handsome too, I don't think I've ever came across a straight guy who ticks all those boxes like you."*

He laughs and says, *"I'm flattered, although the gay community will be in mourning as I most certainly am straight. I've just worked very hard on reinventing myself and my mindset so that I can walk in the shoes of a man I've always wanted to be and admire."* *"Well, it most certainly works so hats off Josh. I think you will have a lot of people who admire you, for the way you carry yourself and your brains."*

We brush hands which makes him take hold of mine. Strolling back towards the hotel, he pulls me in close and looks in my eyes. Brushing my hair off my face he whispers softly, *"Fate brought me to you. You don't even know how amazing you are."* And with that we shared what I could only describe as the softest but most intense kiss I had ever experienced. For once I felt seen and, for the first time, held.

As the plane landed back on UK soil, I was still in a daze at what had happened.

Only I could go away for a relaxing holiday, fall arse over tit in a unicorn float, end up on a fucking stage covered in snotters and tears before falling deeply in lust with my very own Tarzan. When I packed my suitcase for the family holiday, I could never imagine this happening, not by a long shot. Now, landing back home and back to reality, life has certainly taken a flip.

A turn of fate has swept me up unexpectedly and thrown me out of my comfort zone. For once in my life that real and raw vulnerability awoke my soul, unleashing that power inside of knowing that there's something greater than my current circumstances, that there's something ready to greet me and take me to where I'm truly meant to belong. All I had to do was just relax and let it flow. Before this happened, I'm not going to lie here, I'd be as relaxed as a monkey with a cactus stuck to its ass! I'd be letting it flow but I'd be swinging along the branches of life gripping on for dear life. So when I think back, my flow was fucked. I was the control freak who doesn't admit that they are one, classic.

With all the change that's incoming, I ask my mum to move in for a while to help. *"I'll pay for your upkeep; I just don't know if I'll get called away at the last minute with all of this and if I do at least I'll know that you are here. It'll just be for a few months until I can see where this is heading. You are the only person who has held me and the girls afloat since their dad's accident and this opportunity could change all our lives. Give me the chance to prove myself and I won't let us down."*

I feel like Buzz Lightyear suddenly, pointing to the sky - 'To cockfinity and beyond!' Mum laughed, *"Yes, of course I will. You know I'd do anything to support all my team. You are, and always have been, my purpose. Seeing you go so far, further than I ever could, for your family fills me with so much pride."*

With a big hug I say to her, *"You know, after losing their dad so young, and me my partner, I really don't know what I'd have done without your support. I know I can do this for us all, I just know it."*

Watch this space. I could rewrite our history and change things to a better future. I could even have my hand held by a knight in shining armour rather than tinfoil. The possibilities seem endless. I just feel this was meant to happen.

"So do I," she said, *"So do I. Go get 'em, tiger. I'm here, go do it."*

ACKNOWLEDGMENTS

This is the awkward part at the back of the book where you hope you don't miss anyone out or they will tear you up for arse paper! So here goes...

My two daughters, without you two I don't think I would be the women I am today, and I mean that with every breath of my being. As a young single mum it's never been easy, but has it been worth it? With every inch of my soul. Seeing you both as young ladies today I am the proudest mum I can be. My only regret has been working so hard when you guys were so young to make ends meet whilst also trying to follow my path. I think if any parent could rewind time to have that back all over again, they would. I know I would in a heartbeat. You guys are my absolute pride and joy, the reason I've been finding life's meaning in my mum pants. And I wouldn't change a damn thing. Xx

My family is that big I'll need to write a second book!

MUM
You are amazing. I couldn't do what I've done over the years without you. You are the backbone for the girls and me. Your love and care for us I can never repay. The times in Spain you gave us I will always hold dear. I am you and you are me, I love you so much. Xx

DAD
My rock and roll rock. The older I get, the more I see myself in you and that's a privilege. I love you dearly daddio. Xx

IAN
My big I McKay, you're a dick! Only kidding, you're my pupa bear and you've guided me through a lot in life with our chats. I appreciate and love you. Xx

CLAIRE
I'm glad you put up with me over the years as I was most likely a little bugger growing up. Thank you for all the travels and opportunities the girls and I have had. We appreciate and love you. Xx

AMY

My crazy little sister Amy. You are always in my corner, either fighting people with hairspray cans or moving me out my millionth house. You are always there no matter what, me and the girls would be lost without you. Always remember that you are something special. Love you always. Xx

GEM

How many times have I lead you astray? Wait, don't say a thing. Even though you live far away you are always close to my heart. I love you and I'm so proud of your achievements in life. Xx

JAMIE

My little big brother Jamie. You're lucky I love your ass the number of times I've had a phone call over the years. Big sis to the rescue, ha-ha! Crazy bastard. I love you loads and always will. Xx

DAVID

My partner David for pushing me to get this finished and chasing my ass up to make sure I was putting in the work to get it done. I did it! Thanks for pushing me, I love you millions. My cheerleader, minus the skirt and crop top, lol. Xx

DIANE

For editing this and being the very first to read this front to back. Lady, I love you. Thank you so much. I appreciate you so much for doing so. You know you have to now edit all my future ones, lol. Xx

RYAN

For hand drawing the image for the front cover. The image is badass and is even better than it was in my head. Mega skills matey, from your tattoos on me to my front cover image. Thank you. Xx

TALIA

Thank you to Talia for her bomb tech skills in bringing Ryan's image to life then formatting and laying out the whole book so it can be in everyone's hands. Girl, you are a lifesaver with your skills. Loved creating another amazing project together. Xx

---

I can't put everyone else in or I'll be here another five years writing this. To all my family, my friends, my friends who are like family, everyone who has been there for me over the years, you know who you are, I love you and I appreciate your love and support.

For everyone else who done me wrong, you made me strong. And I hope your next shite is a hedgehog! Love and peace.

To Help You Find Your Life's Meaning In Your Mum Pants!

Join my community on Facebook which is a closed private group
_ @ **Caramella magick of the mind**

This is a closed community of uplifting content, local meet ups, chats, mum shit and witchy shit to help us all with the madness of being human and navigating this space in the universe.

Follow me on my podcast at 'Finding Life's Meaning in your Mum Pants' obviously. I look forward to welcoming you into this closed space and community. I also can't thank you enough already for your support in making my dreams a reality and spreading my mad ass glitter to you. Watch this space, the second in this series won't take five years, I promise!

Printed in Great Britain
by Amazon

40908081R00046